EMARA'S CHALLENGE

Cover Design: Diana TC, triumphbookcovers.com
Design: Diana TC, triumphbookcovers.com
Author Photo: Monica Flores
Editing: Kristy S. Gilbert

ISBN Print: 978-0-578-63475-3
ISBN Electronic: 978-1-7923-3028-5

EMARA'S CHALLENGE

MONICA FLORES

This book is dedicated to my six amazing children and my wonderful husband, who continue to support me and my dreams. Thank you for being part of our family. Without you, this family would be missing something wonderful. Each of you is special. I love you.

CONTENTS

ACKNOWLEDGMENTS

I NEVER KNEW HOW HARD it was to write and publish a book until I did it. This story plagued me for many years until I wrote it down, but even with that there was still a lot of work to be done. When I finally did write it, I first shared some chapters with some wonderful friends, Craig and Linda Allen, who encouraged me to continue writing.

Despite some wonderful teachers, English was my weakest subject in school. I now have to lean upon those whose skills are greater than my own. To my editor, Kristy S. Gilbert, who read my second draft, I sincerely apologize for its content. Your editing skills are amazing and continue to steer me toward self-improvement. I could not have done this without your assistance. To Henry, one of my sons, who loves English, thank you for stepping in and being involved in the making of this book. Your editing skills and input are always appreciated and have helped make Kristy's life so much easier after her first round of editing.

To my friend, Dr. Adrian Harvey, thank you for taking

the time to answer my medical questions in an effort to provide correct details. If there is an error, the author is entirely to blame.

To my cover designer, Diana TC, who listened to my idea and brought it to reality, you are quite talented. Thank you for making such an amazing cover for my book.

To my friends and friends-of-friends who have already jumped the hurdle of publishing books, thank you for your time and talents. Thank you to Taylor Dean, Jason DeGray, Kasey Stockton, and Wendy Passantino for allowing me to bombard you with many questions and for your continued support. Cynthia Anderson, thank you for believing in me and encouraging me forward, answering all my questions. Thank you to all of you for supporting me throughout this journey. If you are not familiar with these authors, please look into their works.

My beta readers are amazing! Thank you Sukyoung Jan, Susan Wahlquist, Kendra Harvey, Vicki Wiesner, Casey Hibbs, and Dorine Campsey. Your ideas, thoughts, and punctuation and spelling error finds helped to whip this story into something I am proud of. My young beta readers, Kate, Krissy, and Mira, thank you for your interest and input. Your enthusiasm and support continue to move me forward toward publication of this work.

This page would not be complete without thanking my sweet husband of over twenty-five years and my wonderful children: thank you for being part of my life.

The most beautiful people are those who have known defeat, known suffering, known struggle, known loss, and have found their way out of the depths. These persons have an appreciation, a sensitivity, and an understanding of life that fills them with compassion, gentleness, and a deep loving concern. Beautiful people do not just happen.

—Elisabeth Kubler-Ross

ARNAC DEFENSIVE STRATEGY

Calene & Suyana   (COMMANDERS)

Omni   Loyola & Eida   (GENERALS)
(over the men)   *(over the women)*

Akna/Mausi   Kanti   Ituha/Zahra   Emara/Chaya   (SERGEANTS)

PROLOGUE

AROUND 23 BC THERE EXISTS a group of people that cover a part of North America. They refer to themselves in two distinct divisions: Nephites and Lamanites. The names started as a way to identify their forefathers, and over time they evolved from family to belief system. The Nephites believe in industry and live to the north-northwest. The Lamanites hunt and forage. At this time the Nephites and the Lamanites have become pretty similar in industry and trade openly with one another. They also have a common enemy, the Gadianton robbers, who selfishly want power by any means.

EMARA

THIS IS MY ESCAPE! SHE stands looking over the valley. *I can think here. It's high, hard to get to, and private. No one can see me except for the birds above.* She looks at Uthal, where she came from, in the distance. How small it looks. The wooden buildings with all their decorations look like little rectangular trees. Even the tall wooden wall around the city with all its elaborate designs seems so small that she could walk over it from up here. The people beyond the wall look like ants scurrying from one place to another inside a four cornered cage. She allows her mind to turn to the problem while her hands absently reach for her braid.

At the Stand I'll have to announce my decision to be bound to a husband within a year or take the Challenge. "I'm *not* ready for a husband." She paces around the plateau. Raising her hands midstride, she shouts at no one in particular, "It's not fair!" She exhales forcefully, recalling that there is a better way to solve problems. Pacing a few more revolutions, Emara finally sits, drawing her knees to her chest and wrapping her arms around them.

She watches as a bird soars overhead, singing a joyful melody while the fresh, cool spring breeze touches her skin. The smells of springtime fill the air even here on this precipice. With a mind of their own, her hands again reach for her braid. "My alternative to a husband is the Challenge, from which no woman has returned. What happened to them? Well"—she bites her lip—"I can defend myself."

"Emara!" a male voice reaches her ears from below, invading her privacy. She wonders who it is and how he found her. "Emara, are you up there?"

Thinking that the guards have found her, she worries that her parents will be informed and what little freedom she has left will be gone. Quietly getting on her stomach, she looks over the edge, trying to see who's below while keeping invisible.

The irritated voice from below sounds again. "Emmy, answer me! I tracked you this far." Only a few people call her that, and they are her brothers and her best friend, Selina. Looking down over the ledge, she sees a man standing far below and looking up, but his face is shaded. "Emmy, answer me! I'm worried something happened to you."

Emara backs away from the ledge and sits, weighing the pros and cons of not answering her brother. Her hands fiddle with her braid. The now quite familiar voice empowers Emara to hope that she can persuade him to not tell their parents. Making a decision, she looks over the ledge. "Enon, is that you?"

"Yes!" Enon looks up toward the sound of Emara's voice, but sees nothing. "Where are you?"

Waving an arm, "Up here."

Shielding his eyes to see better, he sees the moving arm. "How did you get up there?"

"I climbed. I'll come down."

Enon grins, knowing his sister is trying to hide something. "You don't have to hurry down. I can come up. Just tell me where to start."

There is a pause that becomes pronounced. Enon hears, "First thing's first. You have to promise *not* to tell anyone about this place."

Looking up at where his sister perches, he hollers, "You've got to be kidding."

"I am serious! This is my place, and I want to keep it private. Promise me."

Enon stands there for a minute, looking at the cliff face, back up to where Emara is, and back at the cliff face. He finally looks up, hollering back, "I promise not to tell anyone."

Even with Enon's promise, Emara sits back, contemplating sharing her world with her older brother. She needs his advice, there is plenty of daylight left, and she's not ready to return to the city. "Come up." She shouts. "Start in the groove where the rock face meets. I could use your help with something."

Enon follows his sister's instructions, finding where to start. "Coming up." As he starts climbing, Emara's thoughts drift as her eyes catch the view in front of her. Her hand absently snakes up, snatching a braid.

"Emmy?" says a deep, concerned voice behind her.

Emara jumps up, ready for an attack. "You scared me!"

Laughing at her response, he says, "Serves you right. You invited me up here and knew that I was coming."

"I was thinking."

Enon's eyes fasten on the view around him. "What a strategic place." Enon looks at the city below. "This is a perfect place to hide while monitoring the valley and the back of the city. When did you find this place?"

"A few years past." Turning to her brother, she glares at him. "Just remember you promised not to tell anyone." Enon nods.

Enon watches his sister as she sits down, tucking her arms around her knees and fiddling with the end of her long black braid while looking out over the precipice. Enon sits down next to his sister. "You always did like to climb. How did you find this place?"

"As you know, Selina and I like to explore. We found a way to get out of Uthal without others missing us. It started off as a challenge to see who could climb the highest." Emara shrugs. "We made it to the top." She looks at her brother. "How did you find me?"

"I saw you leave with your guards after we took you home this morning. Being that it was still too early means you were up to something, so I followed you. I sent your guards home, and they will tell anyone who asks that you're with me."

"Where are your guards?"

Enon grins at Emara. "Standing where you left your guards. That's pretty inventive, making a rope to climb out a window." He reaches over and retrieves the waterskin that is available. After taking a drink, he wipes his mouth and replaces the cap, deciding to get to the point of what is bothering Emara. Nudging Emara's shoulder with his own, he says, "What's bothering you? Is it a boy?"

"Stop it!" She glares at him. "You know I don't like anyone around here. They're stupid. If I did like someone, you all would know about it and tease me mercilessly."

Surprised by her reaction, Enon holds up his hands. "All right, Emmy, I'll stop. What's troubling you?"

Emara is quiet for a few moments, thinking of how to voice her concerns. "It's not fair."

"What's not fair?"

"Now that I'm in my sixteenth year, I have to choose whether to be joined to a man or take the Challenge. None of you have to do that."

"Wait a second, I'm not understanding."

"You, Helam, Hezekiah, and Telah are not being forced to be joined or take the Challenge. Why am I? I'm the youngest."

"As far as I know, you're not being forced. You have a year to decide who to accept to be your husband. Now, on the other hand, I feel sorry for Helam. His spouse has been chosen for him, and he's not even met her. He was supposed to be joined several years back. I don't know how he managed it, but has been able to defer it until later this year. I think I know why he's waited so long."

Surprised, Emara looks up at Enon. "Why?"

"I'm pretty sure he loves Selina and he has waited because he's trying to figure out a way to be joined to her. I don't know how he's going to make that happen."

"I didn't know that he had an arranged Joining. We're all together every morning for my self-defense lesson. Why don't I know that?"

"I thought you were smart? We're not Nephites who can choose for themselves, Emara. We are Lamanites and sometimes have arranged spouses. Helam is crown prince. Of course it is arranged. Helam doesn't like to talk about it, so he doesn't bring it up."

"Of course I know that Uthal sometimes has an arranged Joining, but I didn't know about Helam. It doesn't seem like something our parents would do to us. They haven't talked about it. Does Selina know?"

"No! And you're not going to tell her, even if she is your best friend." Emara frowns at her brother. "As commerce with the Nephites has grown, we have also accepted some of their beliefs. This was arranged many years ago, and there wasn't a reason for you to know about it."

"Why can't I tell Selina? She needs to know. She loves Helam, and I know she wants to be joined to him."

"And he to her, but until Helam can figure out a way to make it happen, he doesn't want to get her hopes up. You know how Selina is. You've grown up with her. She will not be available to choose to be joined until after the Journey. We have until then to help Enon out."

Emara nods, "I will help where I can, but I don't know what to do. They should be able to be joined. Being second oldest, did our parents arrange a wife for you?"

"I'm so glad they didn't. I think I would be upset about it."

"But what about me? At the end of this year, if I still don't want a husband, then Father will decide for me." She took breath. "I am not ready to be joined to any man, but the only other choice I have is the Challenge. None of the other women ever come back from it. Their guardian does, but they don't." Enon sits still, waiting for Emara to finish while Emara looks out at the scenery. "I'm scared." When she looks up at Enon, a tear streams down her cheek, which she quickly wipes away. "What is going to happen to me?"

Emara looks away from her brother, blinks a few times, and takes some steadying breaths. Enon's voice breaks through the silence between them. "You're going to have to decide for yourself. If you say you're not ready to be joined, then I suggest you work on trying to decide who's going to be your guardian."

"What? I can't believe you'd say that knowing I won't return."

With a sigh Enon says, "Some return."

"They do?"

"Yes. They do. I happen to have a friend whose wife took

the Challenge and returned. If you want, tomorrow I'll take you to meet her."

Emara watches her brother's face. "Would you really?" Enon nods his head seriously.

Emara's face lights up "Yes. I want to go."

"Good. Let's go home." Enon stands up, picks up the waterskin, and looks at the view.

Emara doesn't move. "Not yet." Enon looks down at his sister, sighs, and sits down again next to her. "Who do I choose for a guardian? I'm told a guardian needs to be a trusted friend who can defend himself. All of you can defend yourselves. How am I going to pick?"

Enon laughs. "You are set on taking the Challenge?"

"No! Yes! Aww, I don't know. I don't want to be joined with anyone right now, and the only other option available to me is the Challenge. I want to figure out my path and then decide from there."

"You can't plan everything, Emmy. Sometimes, life just happens."

"But I can plan this. Help me decide."

"Then will you be willing to return home?"

"Yes. I promise."

"I think Hezekiah and Telah are too young to be a guardian."

"So that narrows it down to Helam and you." Enon nods his head. "Selina will never forgive me if I take Helam."

"You know that if you asked Helam to be your guardian, he would do it even if Selina was upset."

"Yes, I know. It would make both of them miserable to be separated, and I don't want to do that to them. Aren't we trying to help them get joined?" Enon laughs. "Seriously, would you be my guardian?"

Enon looks at his sister. "I would like nothing better."

Relief rushes through Emara, and she gives her brother a hug. "Thank you."

"My responsibilities can be given to Hezekiah and Telah. It's time they grew up." Grinning, Enon looks at his sister. "Good. Now we can get back to the city. Ready?" Emara nods.

They climb down the cliff face and hurry back toward the brown rope that is hanging outside the window, blending with the wall. Emara takes the lead climbing the rope. She has done this many times, making quick work of it. Enon, however, takes more time working himself up the rope. When he gets in through the window, he sits on the floor. Emara pulls up the rope and hides it in a box that is sitting in the opposite corner from the window.

"It amazes me how well thought out all of this is," Enon says. "How did you find this place?"

"We wanted a place to go where we could talk—without someone listening to our conversation. Selina is the one who found this place and brought me here. We worked out a plan to keep it a secret. It's like everyone has forgotten this place even exists. We've cleaned it up just a little bit."

"What made you want to go outside the city?"

Emara shrugs, "Adventure."

"Emmy," Enon sighs, "It's not safe out there."

"Who says?"

"I say."

Emara glares at her brother. "I've been doing just fine for the last several years."

"You've been with Selina—"

"Until she got that governess. Even without Selina, I haven't had any problems and I've met no one."

"Promise me, Emmy, you will *not* go outside the city again on one of your adventures without me."

"Why? So I can have a babysitter?"

"Because I am your brother and don't want anything bad to happen to you."

"I'm fine!"

"No, you're not! What if someone finds your rope and pulls it up while you're outside the city wall? What then?"

"What does that mean?"

"It means that a lot of people care about you and will be worried about your safety. Since you asked me to be your guardian, I would feel better if I were with you."

"Oh!" She looks out the window, and her hand reaches for her braid. Enon grins, knowing that she is thinking it through. Finally, the hand falls, and Enon quickly wipes the grin off his face before Emara faces him. "I promise. Just so you know, it is because I decided. Not because you said so."

Enon chuckles at his sister's further display of independence. "Good. Let's get going. Do you have Helam's letter with you?"

"Yes."

"Selina is fortunate that she went to school with you so she knows how to read and write."

"She is, but it helped me having her at school."

"How so?"

"Selina is very smart. She's helped me so many times in understanding concepts that were presented. I couldn't have passed the classes without her. Furthermore, she is so gregarious that I didn't stand out with her next to me."

"How are you getting the letter to Selina?"

"I was going to visit her." Enon nods and gestures toward the stairs. Emara steps past her brother, leading the way down the stairs and out the door, closing it securely behind them. They stop for a moment, blinking as their eyes adjust to the bright sun. Enon's guards stop talking and quickly follow behind them as they move through the city streets toward Selina's home.

Once at the front of Selina's house, Emara touches Enon's arm, indicating he should block the view of the guards for a moment. Enon steps in front of his sister, and a guard knocks on Selina's door. Emara discreetly pulls Helam's letter out of her pocket, stuffing it in her shirt without others seeing. When she is done, she touches her brother's arm. The door opens, revealing a servant, and they are directed inside to wait for Selina's mother.

"Since it is late in the day, this will be a short visit. Understand?" Emara nods.

"Enon and Emara, how wonderful to see you both."

"It's good to see you as well, Abish. I'm wondering if Emara can visit for a little bit while I talk with Lahonti."

"Of course she can."

"Abish, you're the best. Thank you." Enon deposits Emara in Selina's mother's care and leaves with his guards. Abish takes Emara down the hall to visit Selina.

Emara reaches the family room, where she finds Selina working on a sewing project. Her governess sits nearby doing some mending. Selina looks up, "Emmy!" Selina drops the sewing to the side and bounces to the doorway, enveloping Emara in a warm hug. "It's so good to see you."

Emara hugs her back and smiles at her. "It's good to see you too. What are you working on?"

She bounces back over to the fabric and holds it up, revealing a man's shirt. "Mother wants me to finish this up before we start the Journey."

"That I do, daughter." Abish takes her place in another chair, resuming her sewing project.

"The shirt is looking good. Mother had me finish my future husband's shirt last year."

"That was when I wanted Selina to do it, and she managed to start it—"

"But I never finished it. Mother, do you mind if Emmy and I go outside for a little bit? This would be a much needed break after working so hard on the shirt today."

Abish eyes her daughter. "You do need to finish the shirt."

"I will, Mother. I promise. Emmy is here to visit, not help us with sewing."

Abish puts down her sewing and smiles at Emara, then looks back at her daughter. "Keep close to the house."

Selina links arms with Emara, talking about her morning while she walks Emara outside with the governess following. When they get a few paces ahead and beyond earshot of the governess, Selina changes the conversation. "I hate sewing. When I am queen, others can do the sewing for me. Do you have something for me?"

"Yes." Emara pulls Helam's letter out of her shirt and passes it to Selina who promptly places it within her pocket without the governess seeing.

"It feels a little thicker. I hope Helam sent more paper." She glances at the governess, who is still trying to catch up.

"Enon knows about the precipice."

"How did that happen?"

"He followed me today."

"That stinks."

"I know. Do you have something for Helam?"

"Yes." Selina stops and points at a bird in the tree, then strategically pulls out her letter to Helam from her waist while Emara matches her enthusiasm for the creature and receives the letter, tucking it into her pocket without anyone seeing. The transaction complete, they resume walking.

Emara watches the governess, who struggles to catch up

to them, while she debates telling Selina about Helam's arranged spouse. "You wear her out."

"I do my best. We leave on the Journey soon. Are you excited?"

"Not really."

"I am. Then I can be joined to Helam." Emara smiles at her friend's enthusiasm while she hopes Helam can make that happen. The governess catches up, and the conversation switches to hairstyles. The girls talk for a little bit and then join the other children in a game of tag. Emara enjoys playing with the others until Enon returns—all too soon for her taste. But she joins him without complaint, and they head home.

They arrive home just as everyone sits down to eat, and their father catches their return. "It is nice to see you two again. We have been wondering what has happened to you. Go wash up, then come eat, and you can tell us all about it."

"Yes, Father," they reply, hurrying off.

Their mother, Suyana, after hearing Gilgal, calls after them, "Glad you are both home safe and sound."

"Last one there is horse manure," Emara challenges Enon, causing a race to start as they hurry to the water room, quickly wash their face and hands, then return to the dining room to eat. Enon barely beats Emara with a grin on his face.

The aroma of the food makes Emara realize that she had only water all day, making her stomach growl loudly. "I'm starving." She drops into the chair as Suyana dishes out a large portion of baked fish, corn, and flatbread, passing plates to Enon and Emara.

After a while, Hezekiah breaks the sounds of the meal being eaten. "Enon, what have Emmy and you been doing today?"

"Yes, what have you and Emara been doing today? We would all very much like to know," booms the patriarch, eying his children.

Emara quickly looks up at Enon, hoping he will not divulge what she has been doing today. He returns her look and turns his attention to his father. "We went walking. Emmy had some questions she wanted to ask me, so I answered them."

Gilgal looks directly at Enon. "Where did you go walking?"

Enon returns his father's look. "Around the city." Emara looks down at her plate, concentrating on her food, hoping that Enon will not elaborate, spilling the fact that they were outside the city wall. "Tomorrow I have some business with Lib to find out when we need to plant. This will take most of the day, and I would like Emmy to go with me. Is that all right?"

"He is a great astronomer, and I look forward to hearing his prediction regarding this year. I do not see why Emara should not join you. Do you have any objections, Mother?"

"It will be good for Emara to be outside. What questions did you have, Emara?"

Emara keeps her eyes on her plate. "I was wondering about being a woman."

Suyana looks at Emara silently, as if recalling herself at sixteen years. Emara wants to squirm, but knowing that will only cause further questions, she decides to remain still. Suyana looks at Gilgal, delivering a silent message, and then looks back at Emara. "You can always come to me, dear, for answers. You do know that, do you not?"

Emara looks up at her mother, "Yes, Mother, I know. Enon was . . . just there at the right time. I've been deciding whether to be bound or take the Challenge."

Suyana puts her hands on the table. "Why are you considering the Challenge?"

"Because I don't want to be joined. I'm not ready for that."

Suyana opens her mouth to speak as Gilgal's hand covers hers and he slightly shakes his head. Emara's eyes widen, seeing her mother's mouth close. Gilgal looks at his daughter. "You know your mother and I will accept your decision, whatever it may be. We have felt something has been troubling you of late, but we have been waiting for you to tell us."

Suyana tries smiling at her daughter. "We know you will tell us when you are ready."

Telah, absorbed with eating, didn't fully listen to the conversation around him. After hearing something about a decision, he looks at his sister. "Emmy, have you made up your mind whether to be bound or take the Challenge?"

"No . . . I haven't."

"Telah, it is time for you to start paying attention to what is going on around you, even when you are eating. It is a skill that will help you in the future."

"So you have mentioned before, but I'm trying." Telah shovels more food into his mouth. Speaking with his mouth full, "It's really difficult when I'm so hungry."

Gilgal shakes his head, turning the conversation toward the day's events, asking each of his children questions and expecting answers. "Helam how are the new recruits?"

"Settling in. They start training tomorrow."

"Do we have a lot of Nephites coming to the city this spring to trade?"

"Around the same number for now, but I suspect more Nephites will trade this year. We have been keeping tabs on our visitors."

"Good. Good. This city was once built by Nephites, and

they put a lot of industry into building a beautiful city. I always worry about them wanting to take it from us."

Telah swallows his food. "In school we learned that we took the area back from the Nephites who invaded and took it from our forefathers. Why do we allow them in the city if you are worried about an attack?"

"Good question, Telah. We did take the land back from the Nephites around thirty years ago. The Nephites are strange people. You can see they create fine work but waste their time on irrelevant things such as carving scenes in the walls of the city."

Emara interrupts. "I like the pictures on the walls. I think they're pretty."

"They may be pretty but serve no purpose." Gilgal turns back to Telah. "We have guards in place to warn us if an army is headed this way. We even have guards that watch our Nephite traders. Nephites don't grow tobacco. Nephites create fine textiles. Lamanites grow tobacco and supply the pipes that are used to smoke the tobacco. This is just a small example of goods that are traded within the city."

Helam continues. "Both Nephites and Lamanites bring their goods here to Uthal to trade, as this is a good place close to the land border and next to the river, where trade can easily take place without issue. Trade makes our city prosper."

Hezekiah scratches his head. "Why do those who travel between the cities carry banners?"

Father smiles at Hezekiah. "Since we have started trading, we look more and more like each other. By having the banners, we know who is a Nephite and who is a Lamanite and what city they come from." Turning to Enon, Gilgal changes the subject. "Enon, when do you think Lib will tell us to start planting?"

"I suspect it will be within the next moon. I shall find out more tomorrow."

"Hezekiah and Telah, how are your studies going? Are you done with your homework?"

"I got mine done."

"Me too."

"What was your homework in?"

"Mathematics."

"Do you understand it?"

"I do now, after Hezekiah helped me with it."

"You are good boys. It is important to do well in school."

"Emara, I heard you visited two friends today. Who did you visit?"

Emara's head pops up from her meal. She quickly shoots Enon a look, then concentrates her attention on her father. "I visited Bamah and Selina today."

Mother's eyes brighten, and she rests her hand on the table. "How are Abish and Selina today?"

Emara's eyes switch to her mother's smiling face. "They are good, Mother. Abish has Selina working on her spouse's shirt, and Selina has promised to get it completed before the Journey." Emara eyes Helam with a grin.

"Is Bamah feeling better?"

"With this beautiful spring day, I think she is."

The conversation led by their father continues around the table until it is time for bed. Emara snuggles down under the soft, warm blanket and closes her eyes, drifting easily to sleep with assurance that tomorrow will be a new day.

DECISION

THE SOUND OF BIRDS SINGING invades her senses, bringing her back to consciousness. Emara stretches, realizing that a beautiful, bright spring day dawned several hours ago. "No!" She springs out of bed, hurrying to dress. "I hope he hasn't left." She flies down the hall, finding Enon finishing breakfast.

Surprised by his sister's entrance, Enon looks up from his food. "I wondered when you were getting up. It's already late, and we've a full day ahead of us if you still want to go."

"I still want to go." Emara plops in a chair. "What's for breakfast?"

"Sweet bread, honey, and leftover fish." Enon takes another bite. "It's really good."

"What?" She eyes the table, validating the contents. "This isn't normal. Where's breakfast?"

"While you were sleeping and I was taking care of business, our brothers ate everything they could get their hands on. They told me, 'You snooze? You lose.' Getting up from the table to leave, he says, "We need to leave soon if you're still going."

"I will have to thank them for eating my breakfast."

"And they're going to reply with the same thing they told me." Enon gently tugs one of Emara's braids on his way out of the room. A short while later, Enon returns with a loaded daypack. "Ready?" Emara stuffs the remaining food into her mouth, nodding to Enon while getting up from the table. She holds up her hands, showing Enon her sticky fingers while she continues chewing. He nods, and she rushes out of the room only to return shortly with a wet face and hands. Grinning at his sister, he picks up the daypack. "Let's go."

Enon and Emara leave the security of their home with Enon's guards following them as they walk toward the other side of the city. "Thank you for letting me sleep in," Emara says. Enon's head slightly nods as he continues his quick pace. "The market's busy today," she adds.

"Did you say something?"

Emara looks at Enon, loudly stating, "The market's busy today."

"I can't hear you over the music. Wait a minute." They continue to weave in and out of traffic, trying to move through the market. The music ends as they get close to the Stand.

Emara turns herself, walking backward so she can continue her conversation with her brother. "I said, the market is busy today." She turns herself around again as her eyes go to the vendor selling clothing.

"It is. Watch out for the performers." Enon pulls his sister to the side as the performers exit the Stand. "You almost walked right into them."

"There's so much to see."

"Not today."

"The food smells good."

"Since we started late this morning, we're not stopping. If you get hungry, let me know. I've brought persimmons." Emara nods, trying to keep up with his quick pace.

"Do you have water?" Enon nods. "I need it."

Enon stops and rummages in the pack, pulling out the waterskin and taking a drink.

"Hey!"

Enon, chuckling, passes the waterskin her way. While she drinks, he pulls out a persimmon, offering it to her. She shakes her head no and passes him the waterskin, which he promptly returns to the pack with the fruit. They continue walking, caught up in their own thoughts while the sun slowly moves across the sky.

"Bamah?"

Emara looks at her brother. "It's the precipice."

"I gathered that. How did you get our parents to think there is a girl named Bamah?"

"Selina and I liked going to the precipice, so we named it. It suits, don't you think? I think the guards overheard us calling it Bamah and reported that we visited our sick friend Bamah." Emara shrugs her shoulders. "We let the story continue." Emara grins to her brother. "Why do you ignore girls?"

"That came out of nowhere. Why are you asking?"

"No reason. I've just noticed you do that and am wondering why."

He looks at her. "Because they know I'm the king's son."

"I bet most of them don't know that, and I bet it's just because you're good looking."

Enon raises an eyebrow at Emara. "You know, you can be very nice when you want to be." His face morphs into a frown. "They know we're the king's children even if we dress as everyday people."

"Since you don't have an arranged spouse, why don't you get to know a woman? I've never seen you even try. Not once. What's so negative about women?"

"Why don't we talk about you? Isn't this outing for you?"

"I believe you said you have business and invited me along. You haven't answered my question."

"I forgot your question on purpose. You can really be annoying at times."

"I haven't. Why are you negative about women?"

"I'm not negative about women."

"You've not gotten to know one."

"Just because you haven't seen me talk to a woman doesn't mean I haven't talked to women."

"So do you like a woman?"

Enon stops and looks at his sister. "All right, Emmy, I give up. I know you won't let this go until you have an answer." Enon starts walking again, this time at a slower pace Emara matches. "I watched Helam as he grew up, and the girls and women would flock to him just because he's heir to the throne. Some would do everything they could to keep his attention, and the both of us got tired of it. Selina is the only girl that didn't drool all over him, hoping to catch him, and she's the only girl that would encourage him to improve himself. I like it that she doesn't put up with any bad behavior from others, plus she is more interested in having fun with you. Both Helam and I were first attracted to her because of that, but before you open your mouth thinking there is something more, let me speak." He waits until Emara closes her mouth. "I haven't been ready to be bound . . . like you . . . until recently. I've started looking for a wife, but so far no woman has caught my eye. I would like to find someone strong like you."

Emara stops. "Like me?"

"Yes. Like you. You know how to defend yourself, and very few women have that skill. You are independent as much as you can be." Enon shrugs. "You are you."

"Thanks, I think." They start walking again.

They continue to move through the city at a quick pace, finally stopping in a quiet street. "We're here." Enon's guard, familiar with this home, announces their arrival by banging on the door and then moves to the side for Enon. The gate opens to a man, shorter than Enon, who has dark brown eyes and black hair and is full of smiles and good cheer.

"Lib, I brought Emara with me," says Enon as his hand moves to the side, introducing his sister.

Lib moves out of the way, making room for Enon and Emara to enter. Lib closes the door and takes Enon and Emara to a pleasantly plump woman, with similar coloring as her husband's, playing with three small children on the ground. She looks up as they come closer and smiles, getting up to walk toward them. When she arrives, Lib introduces his wife, Ziva, to Emara.

"It's so good to finally meet you. Enon tells us a lot about your adventures. Please come and sit down. Oh my, I've embarrassed you both. I didn't mean to do—"

Lib's gentle arm on his wife's shoulder stops her words, and he smiles at Emara and Enon. "Ziva has no filter. She says what she thinks, and I love her for that."

"My mouth has always gotten me in trouble. Boy, has it." Her frown changes to a smile, and she shows them to the chairs nearby.

Three young children rush over to Enon, squealing their delight. One by one, Enon picks them up and twirls them around, giving them each a big hug, and places them back on the earth. The children laugh joyfully. "Emmy, these are Lib and Ziva's children, and they are a delight." Enon looks in the daypack and pulls out three persimmons, handing each child a piece of fruit.

"You spoil them, Enon." Ziva laughs as she sits in a chair. The youngest climbs on her lap, handing her persimmon to her mother, who takes a bite and hands it back to her daughter. The other girl sits on the ground next to Ziva with the persimmon, and the oldest, a boy of no more than six years, stands on the other side of his mother and starts eating his persimmon. All of the children are full of smiles and interest in what will occur next. "Lib told me you were coming this morning but didn't explain why."

Emara's eyes drop to her lap while she keeps the strained smile on her face. Enon sees his sister's distress and turns his attention to Ziva. "It's time for Emmy to choose to be bound or take the Challenge. She's struggling to make up her mind, and I thought if I brought her here, you may be able to help her through this with your experience with the Challenge."

Lib looks at Emara and then at his surprised wife. "Now, if you will excuse us, we'll take these messy children and let you two talk." Lib picks up the youngest child, who has a death grip on the persimmon while she gnaws and sucks on it. Lib laughs, walking away with her. Enon gets up, and the two oldest children follow the men while holding their persimmons in one hand and wiping the juice off their faces with the other. After a moment they're gone leaving the two of them.

"I'm so sorry about embarrassing you," Ziva says. Emara looks up at Ziva. "When I was younger I always got into trouble." Ziva smiles. "It's my mouth." She winks at Emara. "My mother didn't know what to do with me, and we were too poor to have someone else watch out for me. Needless to say, I always managed to make it out of my scrapes . . ." Ziva smiles again. "With help." Ziva looks at Emara. "Your brother worries about you and sometimes asks for advice." Placing her hands on her knees and leaning forward, Ziva looks directly at Emara. "I've heard from Enon, but I haven't heard from you. What brings you here today?"

Emara looks down for a moment, summoning her courage to speak with Ziva. She takes a steadying breath and raises her eyes again. "I . . . really don't know where to start." Emara takes another breath, trying to smile. "This year, I'm to become a woman, and we leave in a moon. I need to decide whether to be bound to a husband or take the Challenge. I'm not ready to be bound, and I don't even have a person in mind. I'm not ready for that, so the alternative is the Challenge. Up until yesterday, I thought that women who take the Challenge never return, but Enon corrected me and told me that you took the Challenge."

"You do know that you have a year to choose who will be your husband?"

"But that's just it, I'm not ready to be bound."

"I see," Ziva states seriously. "What questions do you have?"

"What happens to the women?"

"The day you return from the Journey with your mother, you again have the Stand. This time you will stand alone. At the Stand you announce that you are taking the Challenge, and you will have that one night to spend with your family. The next morning by sunrise, you must be outside the city gates with your guardian. This did not occur for me because I did not come back from the Journey with the rest of the women."

"Why?"

"My mother got sick, and I didn't want to leave her at Arnac, so I stayed behind until she got better. Because of that, my journey started in Arnac."

"But you had your mother?"

"For a short time she was with me." Ziva frowns, recalling the memory.

"What happens if you're not outside the city gates by sunrise?"

Ziva looks directly at Emara. "The woman will forfeit her life, so you must be sure about your choice. There's no particular place to go like for the Journey, so you get to go where you want to go. You'll experience many new things, good and bad, and while you're experiencing them you learn a lot about yourself and the world around you. It is very hard, so you must be sure about your decision. You have heard that some don't return?" Emara nods. "You cannot return to Uthal until after the Stand for the next year of women. I was lucky because I returned . . ." Sadness fills Ziva's face again. "But my mother and my guardian did not."

"What happened to them?"

"They died protecting me."

"Oh, I'm so sorry." Emara looks down and frowns, realizing they died during the Challenge.

Ziva laughs, surprising Emara. Catching her attention, she says, "It was a long time ago."

"What happened after they died?"

"The Challenge continued and became much harder."

"How come most of those that take the Challenge don't return to the city?"

Ziva pauses, gathering her thoughts before continuing. "Part of the Challenge is finding your own way until you find where you're most happy. It may be in another city, town, or village. When a guardian feels his charge has found her happiness, whatever that location may be, he'll be free to return and report, or his duty ends at his death. I think all guardians want their charge to be happy. I found where I was most happy, so I returned to Uthal when my year was over. When

I returned it was without fanfare like the Journey. You return quietly."

"If that is the case, why do few women choose the Challenge?"

Ziva chuckles. "Because it's not for everyone. It's very dangerous, probably more so now, and very difficult."

"Then why have it?"

Ziva looks down for a minute before lifting her head. "Because there are women, like us, who must learn through experience. We like figuring things out or"—she winks—"aren't ready to be joined. Perhaps it's because we would not learn the great truth of life otherwise."

"What's the great truth of life?"

Ziva smiles. "That . . . you've got to figure out for yourself."

"Just one more question. Would you recommend it?"

"The Challenge isn't for everyone. It's very, very difficult. But I learned things that I would never have learned if I hadn't taken the Challenge. I've a wonderful life, and I owe part of that to the Challenge." Looking at Emara directly, she adds, "I cannot make your choice for you."

Emara nods.

Emara and Ziva continue talking, becoming fast friends. After some time, Lib returns, holding a platter upon which sits a carved clay pitcher, cups, and sliced potato. Enon, happily grinning, is carrying three giggling children hanging off various body parts. Lib delivers the drinks and snacks to a grinning Ziva, who pours water into the cups and passes them out. Turning to the children as she sits down in her chair, Ziva states, "Children, go play a game, and I will play with you when I am done." The oldest of the three children takes his siblings' hands, and they go farther away, starting a simple game of tag with each other. "They are such good children." She passes out the snack to her guests. The men sit in the other chairs, and the group talks happily about current events for a little while longer. Enon finishes his drink and looks at the sky. "Emmy did you get all your questions answered? We need to leave soon if we're going to be home before dark."

"Yes, thank you for bringing me." Emara stands up and everyone follows her lead. "Ziva, thank you so much for answering all my questions. I've so enjoyed meeting you."

"I've also enjoyed meeting you." Ziva takes Emara's cup and deposits it near the pitcher, then gives Emara a hug. "Come back any time, but don't come by yourself. It is a long way, which means you need to bring someone with you to keep you safe." Lib takes the remaining cups, dropping them with the others near the pitcher while Ziva gives Enon a hug. "It is always a pleasure to see you, Enon." Ziva turns to both of them and smiles. "Come back when you can."

Lib conducts Enon and Emara to the gate. "Come again, the both of you." Enon and Lib slap each other on the back, then Enon leads Emara out of the gate.

Waiting for Enon and Emara on the other side of the entry are the guards playing a game with several small stones. The game quickly ends when the two siblings walk through the door and start walking home—their companions quickly join them a few paces behind.

CHOICES

THEY QUICKLY WALK THROUGH THE streets on their return home. "Well, how was it?"

"It was wonderful, Enon. It helped so much talking with Ziva. She is so content and cheerful. The both of them are." She chuckles. "She definitely doesn't have a filter." Grinning, Emara shoots Enon a look. "You seem happy too—playing with their children."

Enon grins back. "Yes, that's part of the fun of my visits with them. I like playing with them, and I'm happy to have Lib and Ziva counted as friends."

"How did you meet?"

"Lib was in school with me for some time, and then he was sent to learn astronomy. When he arrived back in Uthal, he sought me out and we picked up right where we left off." Emara nods. After a little while Enon interrupts Emara's thoughts. "So . . . do you know what choice you're going to make?"

Emara looks up at Enon briefly as they continue walking,

"No. I don't know. Ziva answered all my questions and made the Challenge not so mysterious for me, but there is more to think about. What business did you and Lib talk about?"

"He's an astronomer, as you've heard, so we discussed when planting should take place."

"When did he say we must start planting?"

"During the next new moon."

They continue silently walking when they arrive at the market. Enon navigates through the walkway, making sure his sister is beside him at all times, while Emara's eyes focus on the contents of the stalls. She eventually stops at a stall and pulls on Enon's sleeve. "Enon, here's a beautiful scarf for Mother. Let's get it for her."

Enon, feeling the tug on his sleeve stops walking, turning to grin at Emara. "You couldn't go through the market without buying something?"

"I can too!" Emara glares at him for a second but then pulls him closer to her. "Look at this scarf. It's so Mother." The light green scarf is a fine linen fabric embroidered with vines and flowers. "This will keep Mother warm when it's cool in the morning, but it's not too thick for when it warms up."

Enon looks at the scarf. "Mother would like the scarf since it's reminiscent of her garden."

"Let's get it for her. Do you have something we can trade?"

"You didn't bring your money?"

"I forgot trying to catch up with you this morning." She grins sheepishly.

A few yards away in front of them, arguing between a vendor and what looks to be a patron escalates into a fight. The scarf is forgotten as Enon pulls Emara back and out of the way of the fight. The guards come forward to protect their charges, looking for another way through the market. Enon takes Emara by the arm and passes her off to the closest guard. "Take her and find another way home while I resolve the conflict." The guard now entrusted with Emara nods his head, handing over one of his knives to Prince Enon, focusing now on the safety of Emara.

She digs in her heals and whispers fiercely, "You are not going to jump in to that by yourself. There are three of us here who can help."

"Emara, I don't have time for this. If something happens to you, I would not—"

"I would not be able to live with myself if something happened to you. I know how to fight—you taught me yourself. You have more chance of succeeding with all of us than without us."

Enon looks at her for a moment, frowning. He looks at the fight, then looks back at Emara and the guards, finally nodding. "I will be the bait, and you are not going to tell my parents about Emara knowing how to defend herself." The guards look at each other for a moment, then turn to Enon, nodding. He turns, starting to walk toward the fight in front of him while one of the guards hollers, "Make way for Prince Enon." The onlookers that hear the announcement and aren't involved part so Enon can move forward. By this time the fight has advanced; now three men beat the vendor while another two load the vendor's goods into bags.

"Stop what you are doing if you value your life," Enon booms, startling the thieves.

The two in the stall drop what they're doing and take off running. The three kicking the merchant stop and look up. The oldest man snarls, "I doubt that, *you* spoiled brat." He pulls out a sword.

Emara's brother fires back, taunting, "Not very fair to pull out a sword when all I have is this small knife." The plain-clothed guards silently work themselves around those watching the scene, moving to the other side, where the two men stand over the beaten man. Emara cautiously watches, mixing with the crowd as the leader continues to march toward her brother, starting the fight between sword and knife. Emara keeps her eyes on the duel. Enon avoids the thrusts from his enemy by using things around him as the audience quickly retreats to a safe distance from the fighters.

Emara grabs a tent pole from a stall that has closed for the day and throws it toward her brother, shouting, "Enon!"

He catches the pole in his hand and starts to respond to the oncoming sword thrusts by hitting the man's hand and arm as he extends it, which makes the enemy angrier. Emara looks where the guards went to find that the accomplices are trussed with their hands behind their backs and their feet bound while the merchant is still lying on the ground, motionless. The guards rush forward to assist Enon, and Emara looks back toward Enon to see him land a few good raps with the tent pole to put the enemy on the ground without his weapon. One of the guards removes the man's sword from the ground and places the tip at the man's throat while another vendor quickly moves forward, offering rope to the other guard so that the leader can be bound.

The man on the ground, now bound, is pulled to his feet and scowls at Enon. "You are going to regret this. You have no idea what's coming."

"Maybe not, but I can't stand by and see evil within my city."

Emara moves toward the beaten merchant to see if he is still alive. When she reaches him, she finds that he is breathing. Several in the crowd pick up the injured man taking him away. "Where are they taking him?"

An older woman comes forward. "They're taking him to the infirmary. Quickly, come with me, my lady, this isn't over." She grabs Emara's shoulders and rushes her into the crowd just as fifteen guards show up fully armed.

Emara smiles, stopping to watch the guards help her brother, but instead the guards quickly surround the prince's guards, their prisoners, and Prince Enon himself. Unexpectedly, the guards' swords are drawn on Enon and his party. Emara opens her mouth to shout, but something stings her arm and there is a shushing sound in her ear. She looks to see who did it only to find the old woman next to her. "I'm sorry, my lady. Please be quiet." Emara looks back at her brother to see that he and his guards are now being put in a neck stockade made for four. The tied-up criminals are being released by the men dressed in guards' clothing.

When the leader of the first group is released from his bonds, he punches Enon in the face. "You stupid prince." When Enon looks up, he has a bloody nose and both of them glare at the other.

The new leader interrupts the glaring contest. "Leave him alone. There will be plenty of time to wreak vengeance." The guards start to push the three in the neck stockade through the street by sword point.

The new leader turns to the crowd. "As you can see, the king's son can also be taken within his own city. Pay your wages to the new king and you will live. If not, we will find you and start killing your family until you comply or are killed."

Emara faces the old woman. "Where are they taking them?"

"To the manager of the market, who declares himself the new king."

"How long has this been going on?"

"It's been gradually getting worse for the last six moons."

"Why has no one gone to the king?"

"They have, but the manager has stopped those that have complained by silencing them."

"Send someone to tell the king while I help Enon!"

"People have already been sent, but you must not help your brother. Everything will turn out well."

Looking around her, she sees potatoes for sale. She quickly maneuvers herself away from the woman, grabs some potatoes, and throws them at the receding guards. The potatoes hit several of the guards and they stop—turning to look where they came from. Emara stands defiant with a potato in each hand. The guards see her, and two guards are dispatched to retrieve the princess. Emara runs, throwing the remaining potatoes at the advancing guards. *Father should be here soon. I just need more time.*

Noticing a stall selling bows and arrows, Emara picks up a bow and several arrows, hoping that the new weapon will work correctly. Pulling back on the bow, she fires the first arrow at the nearest guard, hitting him in the thigh. *That will slow him down.* She shoots the next arrow at the next guard, hitting him in the upper leg as well. She loads her last arrow, firing upon the leader, but he moves at the last second, allowing the arrow to hit a vertical piece of wood on display in a stall. The leader sends a few more guards, who now pull out their swords. She grabs a few more arrows, ducking under the stall and out the other side. She runs farther up the row of stalls and ducks under the stall again, coming back into the row where her brother is being held. Emara stays low and fires two shots, hitting soldiers in the calf. She ducks back under the stall and runs to a different point and comes back to the stall with the weapons, grabbing more arrows to shoot again. She looks up to see a knife at her brother's throat, stopping her in her tracks.

"Drop your weapon," the leader shouts.

She drops her bow and arrows at her feet while Enon looks at her like she was wrong in trying to save him. Two guards come her way and one of the guards slaps her hard, throwing her to the ground. Under her hand she feels an arrow. Blinking away the stars and tears that sting her eyes, she picks up the arrow as she is dragged from the ground by her hair. When she gets her feet under her she takes the arrow and rams it into the inner thigh of the guard. He cries out in pain, releasing her, but before she can move out of reach the other guard, he catches her by the arms, wrenching them behind her. Searing pain shoots through her shoulders, and she falls to her knees. Her hands are tied behind her as blood drips from her nose and mouth. She watches with satisfaction as the wounded hobble back to the group of guards. The knife is removed from Enon's throat, and the guard that has her begins to walk her by her braid, forcing her toward the stockade. Emara digs in her heels, trying to stay away from the stockade.

Thundering surrounds them, and Emara looks up from her task to find every passage around them blocked by armed guards while the crowd shrinks back farther.

"Release my children!" roars from somewhere.

She looks toward the voice, finding her father with fury radiating from him while he sits upon his mount with his sword raised. The leader of the fifteen turns to the king and reverently bows, hollering back, "Your Majesty, we were just in the process of returning your children safely home."

"Not by that means." The king lowers his raised arm, orchestrating the release of arrows upon the phony guards and the others who started the fight. Emara falls to the ground with the guard who has her hair as he is struck. She quickly kicks and pushes herself away from the body holding her while the king's guards rush forward, finishing the death blows. The king's guards release Enon, Emara, and their plain-clothed companions from their bands, taking the offspring to the king as he dismounts. Gilgal grabs his children, engulfing them in a thankful hug, then looks upon the both of them. Gilgal gently strokes Emara's injured face, frowning.

"How did you know?"

"When a large group descends upon the palace stating my children are in trouble, I respond. Now what caused all this?"

Enon quickly sums up his story.

Emara touches her father's arm, getting his attention. "But there's more. I'm told that the manager of the market has proclaimed himself king and is extorting money from the merchants. If they don't pay, he starts killing a member of the merchant's family until he complies, or they end with killing the merchant."

Gilgal nods his head and turns to the crowd. "Thank you for taking care of my children. Who among you will speak for the merchants?"

An older man steps forward. "I will, as I have no kin left they can hurt."

The king nods. "Very well. Is what my daughter says true?"

"Yes. It's a repeat of what caused our previous war— pride."

"What is the will of the people?"

"We stand with our king to maintain our freedom and our family."

"Com!" The named guard comes to the king's side. "Return

my daughter to the queen." Turning to Enon and placing his hand on his son's shoulder, he says, "It is time to work."

Enon nods.

"Father, why are you sending me away?" Emara asks.

The king turns to Emara with pain in his eyes, "Because it is time to do the least likeable thing there is as king for the benefit of the people. Those that trod on another life for their personal benefit in turn forfeit their own, and I do not want you to be a part of it." He gently touches her bruised face. "Go home. Your mother is sick with worry." Taking Emara's hand, he places it in Com's hand. "Keep her safe."

Com nods, pulling Emara away. Emara is placed on a horse, and a group of the elite guards head for the palace as Emara blinks back tears.

When she arrives at the palace, Suyana rushes to her side. "Emara, what happened?"

Reunited with her mother, she finds that all her brothers are absent. "Mother, I'm fine."

"You are not fine. There is blood all over you. Your eye is swollen shut and the left side of your face looks bruised." Suyana leads her daughter toward the infirmary.

Once in the infirmary, Suyana takes Emara to the single private room and begins to clean her injuries while Emara tells her mother what happened, leaving out her fighting with the soldiers. "Father, your brothers, and the people of this city will unite tonight to protect the city from people who feel that being in a place of power is a privilege and not a place of service. Having power or authority means that there is greater responsibility. These people want the power and authority, but not the responsibility that comes with it."

"Will they be all right?" Emara asks.

"Your father and brothers will be just fine. Father knows

what to do, and so do your brothers." Suyana stands back, looking at her handy work. "Luckily, your wounds will heal. Whose blood is all over you?"

"There was blood on the ground. I must have fallen in it."

"Your eye will take some time to heal, and we will see what it looks like in the morning. In the meantime, this plaster will help." Suyana applies the cloth with the herbs to the affected eye and has Emara hold it while she ties it in place with another cloth. "Now that we have your wounds dressed, it is time for you to change out of those clothes." She goes to the door and opens it enough for a servant to enter with Emara's clean clothes. Suyana and the servant start helping Emara get clean and changed. When Emara's arm is raised, Emara winces, revealing a hurt shoulder, and Mother immediately turns her attention to the injury.

"It is just a mild sprain, and you are lucky that it isn't worse. It will be sore for a few days, and you are not to be picking up anything. If you need help dressing, ask for it." Once finished, the servant gathers up Emara's dirty clothes and leaves the room. Suyana continues, "You look so much better. While the men work, we to must do our job. Come. There is much to be done here to prepare for casualties." Suyana commands and works with everyone around her to prepare for the influx of casualties and soldiers.

Once the tasks have been completed, Emara looks around the room of the infirmary. It is a large room minus the private room. Throughout the night many beds have been added as well as stools next to them for the injured and their family members.

Early in the morning, the casualties start to arrive. "You can put him here." Suyana points to the nearby bed. The two men carrying the man deposit him on the bed. A priest and some women immediately descend upon him, beginning their work. "Thank you. If you would like, go to the great hall where there is food and drink before you set out again." The men nod, heading out the door following others as they walk toward the great hall.

Sometime later, one of the servants touches the queen on her arm and speaks to her softly. Suyana frowns and nods, turning to briefly speak to two other women. One woman stays, taking over Suyana's responsibility while the other woman follows the queen, arriving next to Emara, who is dressing an injured man's wounds. The woman takes over the task from Emara, and Suyana pulls Emara out of earshot of the others. "We are needed at home." Grabbing a healing pack from a table, mother and daughter hurry home.

They arrive home to find five filthy, bloodstained men—their men. Suyana quickly hands the healing pack to Emara and falls into her husband's arms. "I'm so glad you are back home. Are you hurt?"

Emara thankfully hugs her brothers and they hug her back while the men reassure the women that they are fine.

"You smell of smoke." The queen looks at the king, "Is it done?"

"It is done. The city is restored to peace and order. The army and the people helped us move through the city swiftly, capturing all involved. It turns out that more than a hundred people were involved. Their dead bodies are burned as well as their homes." Gilgal sighs. "They no longer exist within the city."

"I am glad. Now, let us get you fed, cleaned up, and in bed."

"I do not want to eat." Gilgal smiles briefly at his wife. He looks up at his children. "Boys, go eat. I will see you tomorrow. Emara, it pains me to see your face like that, but I am glad that it will heal." Suyana and Gilgal walk away, leaving the siblings together.

Helam runs a hand through his hair, scattering the dirt and grime as it sprinkles onto his shoulders. "I feel like Father. I have no appetite, but I am glad that we are all home safe. Emmy, your forethought to put up a fight saved Enon. Thank you. I'll see you tomorrow." He heads out the door.

Enon quickly kisses Emmy's injured face. "Thanks, sis." Then he dashes after Helam and stops him briefly by putting a hand on his shoulder and joins him. "Wait for me. I don't want to eat either."

Hezekiah's stomach growls loudly, and Emara smiles at her remaining brothers. "I suppose the both of you need food."

Telah looks at his brother. "As much as we both don't want food, I think our bodies need it."

During times of strife, the great hall gets converted to a dining area, and Emara takes her brothers there to get some food. They enter the great hall, which now contains rows and rows of tables and benches. The food is prepared buffet style so that those who eat can choose what they like. Her brothers pick out the food they want to eat, and she then guides them to a table where a pitcher of water and some cups are delivered. Sitting at the table, she watches her brothers slowly eat the food on their plates, not looking up.

"Is there anything else you need?"

They shake their heads slowly.

"Would you like to talk about it?"

They look up at her for a moment and frown at her.

"What can I do to help?"

The brothers look at each other. Hezekiah turns to Emara. "You already did help by not letting them take Enon. We will be fine, Emara. We just need time. You go ahead and go to bed. You've earned it. We will follow shortly."

She eyes them for a minute, frowning. "All right." Getting up from the table, she gives Telah a hug. "Good night, Telah." Next, she moves over to Hezekiah, giving him a hug. "Good night, Hezekiah." Looking at both her brothers from the end of the table, she smiles. "I'm so glad you both made it safely home. I hope the both of you feel better in the morning."

WORK

THE POULTICE ON HER EYE fell off during the night and lies in its cloth on the bed next to her. "I've overslept again." She raises her arm to hit her pillow and winces. Slowly she rolls out of bed, working her sore muscles as she stands up. She doesn't want to be a burden, asking another to help her dress, so she does it herself, which takes twice as long, as her muscles scream at the movement. Finishing her braids, Emara heads for the kitchen, moving as quickly as she can, continuing to work through her soreness.

She grabs a persimmon from the kitchen, eating it while she walks to the infirmary to start her shift. When she gets there, her mother greets her warmly with a hug. "Mother, how are you able to do this? My whole body hurts!"

Suyana chuckles. "I was not the one injured. Come, let me see your face and shoulder." Pulling Emara into the procedure room, she goes to work. "The men are doing well, and Father has already made his rounds." Suyana gently touches the swollen area around Emara's left eye. "Your face has a lot of blood under the surface. Leeches will help reduce the swelling and improve the color." She applies the leeches to Emara's cheek. "We lost a few good men. Father and your brothers will be with the families of the deceased for the rest of today." While the leeches feast on Emara's blood, Suyana examines her shoulder again. "Still sore, I see." She prepares some tea and hands it to Emara to drink. "This will help with the pain and inflammation." While Emara sips the bitter tea, Suyana continues talking. "The men here in the infirmary are resting comfortably, and their families have started showing up to care for them. Those that are healthy enough will leave today." The leeches start falling off, and Suyana puts them back in their bowl. "Father has called for a day of mourning, which will be held tomorrow." Once the last leech is back in its bowl, Suyana smiles, looking at Emara. "Let us see what we can do to help those that are here."

The day progresses in a blur, with Emara helping the injured and their families receive the rest and comfort they need. Emara smiles, watching family members reunite. Little is said about yesterday's events—everyone knows exactly what was done—but much is said about Emara's facial injury.

The mother of the patient in the next bed interrupts Emara's thoughts as she finishes a fresh dressing to a deep leg wound. "Thank you for caring for my son. He seems to be resting comfortably thanks to you." Emara looks at her son. He's about Hezekiah's age and is smiling at Emara in a way that makes her uncomfortable. Emara frowns inside but smiles at the mother. "All of us here have taken care of your son."

"Mother, she's quite beautiful despite her injured face, and she has such a talent for healing." The son turns his head toward Emara again. "My lady, when I am back on my feet, may I come and visit you?"

"It will be many moons until you are restored to full health. How about you take it one day at a time and see where that leads?" Looking at the family, she says, "Can I get you water? Food? Do you need something?"

"Bless you. Some food will be nice."

"While your son rests, let me show you to the great hall, where there is an assortment of food." The father and mother follow her out, leaving the son to himself.

When she returns to the infirmary, Selina calls Emara over to help re-dress a wound. This wound is on the man's chest. Emara helps Selina secure the dressing by wrapping clean cloth around the injured torso, tying the ends together. He thanks his caregivers with a slight nod and returns to a lying position upon the bed. As Selina and Emara leave the man, Suyana calls them over. "Selina and Emara, thank you for your help today. It is time for both of you to head to the great hall to eat while I will finish up here and meet you in a little while."

Selina looks over to her mother, Abish, and her governess, seeing that they are busy. Selina turns her attention back to the queen, grinning broadly. "Thank you." She mouths. Loudly, so Abish and her governess will hear, "Come on, we've been given a task." Bouncing next to Emara, she links Emara's good arm with hers. When they leave the infirmary Selina leans close to Emara. "Now, what happened? All I know is that Father and my brothers were called to arms and Mother and I to the infirmary."

As they walk, Emara tells her story. They arrive in the great hall, and Emara's stomach growls, making Selina giggle, and both girls rush to get in line for food.

"I'm so glad that they were able to get there in time to save you both. How horrifying."

After filling up their plates, they sit down at a table, and while they eat they begin talking about the Journey, which is just a few weeks away.

"What a nice surprise," Helam states, interrupting their conversation as he sits down next to Selina.

Selina smiles happily at him as Emara's other brothers sit down at the table as well. "It is wonderful to see all of you."

Telah takes a flatbread and tears it. "How did you get rid of the governess?"

"Or your mother?" Hezekiah shoves some food in his mouth.

Selina grins and states, "It's thanks to your mother." The siblings look at each other. "She told us to come eat. I think she will bring my mother and that horrid governess."

"I will have to thank Mother for that." Helam smiles at Selina as they link hands under the table. The group continues eating while making small talk together.

After a little while, Suyana shows up with Abish and the governess. Suyana continues her conversation with Abish and the governess as they sit at the end of the table. Gilgal and the rest of Selina's family show up a little while later, taking the other side of the table. Gilgal, seeing what is taking place between Helam and Selina under the table, frowns, which causes Selina to blush and let go of Helam's hand. Selina's father, Lahonti, also stops the hand holding by sitting between Helam and Selina while the conversation between the two men continues without missing a beat. Selina and Helam concentrate on finishing their food, and the rest of the children do the same. Once Emara and Selina are done eating, they get up from the table.

Suyana stops her conversation midstride and looks toward Emara and Selina. "Will the both of you look back on the injured in the infirmary before leaving for the night?"

"Yes."

Suyana turns her attention to her sons. "Boys, will you please help Selina and Emara in the infirmary?"

Emara's brothers get up from the table, nodding their heads as they stuff another bite of food in their mouths.

Abish looks toward Selina. "Selina, once you are done with the injured, you are to immediately return to the great hall and report to me."

"Yes, Mother."

Lahonti looks at his sons. "Join your sister and help with what is required of her."

"We're not done."

Their father glares at them. "You can eat again afterwards." The brothers get up at their father's words.

The group leaves the hall together. Once they are outside, Helam grabs Selina's hand, causing a big smile to light her face once again as the group walks slowly toward their destination. Ogath, Selina's brother, falls in step beside Helam.

Helam says, "I'm glad you are for Selina and me getting joined."

"I don't think our parents are," Ogath returns.

When they arrive at the infirmary, they make a plan. Helam and Selina work together on one side of the infirmary while Emara and the rest make quick work on the other side of the infirmary. They check the patients, making sure their pain is controlled, they feel comfortable, and their needs are taken care of. Bandages that need changing are dressed. They check that the injured have fresh water and clean chamber pots within the infirmary. Once Emara completes her side of the room, she takes over Selina's remaining tasks with her brothers help. Helam and Selina walk to the corner of the room to talk with one another while Ogath and Shum, Selina's brothers, stand out of earshot but within sight of Selina.

When everything is completed, the group walks toward Helam and Selina, who are deep in conversation. Ogath coughs a couple times, causing Selina and Helam to look up, frowning. But then, seeing everyone, they join the group without word. They walk slowly and quietly back toward the great hall, allowing more time for Helam and Selina to be together before returning her to Abish.

The next morning arrives quickly. Emara walks into the great hall to see that there is cold corn, beans, bread, and jerky to eat. She makes a plate and joins her mother at a table as Suyana looks upon her. "Your face is getting better, although the color will look worse a little while longer. To-day is a day of mourning, which means no fires will be lit and meals will be simple. The city will celebrate those who lost their lives a few days ago and honor the families who lost someone. When you are done eating, come join me in the infirmary, as the injured need looking after before we head to the Stand."

When Emara finishes eating, she slowly walks to the in-firmary, enjoying the warm sunshine. She arrives once again to see her mother busy supervising the day's activities.

"Emara, it is good to see you." Suyana greets her daughter. "Are you ready?" Emara nods. "Good. Can you please take the dirty laundry to get washed?"

Emara looks at her mother and smiles. "Yes."

Suyana smiles back. "Someone is to help lift and remove the baskets. Do you understand?"

Emara nods.

"Do you know why I assign you chores that other people can do?"

"So I get to be outside?"

"It is so you understand that even though you are a princess, you are not above anyone else."

"Is this what you were trying to explain to me the other day about power coming with responsibility?"

"Partly, my dear. So much can be learned from work. Part of being a woman is knowing how to keep a home. Knowing how to do things for yourself provides you freedom. Working as others do keeps you grounded. When you are a leader, others will be willing to follow because you are right there working with them. So many things can be learned from work." Suyana gives Emara a hug and points her in the direction of the dirty clothes. Leaning close to Emara's ear, she adds, "It is also so you can be outside."

Emara smiles fondly at her mother, then gathers up the dirty laundry into a large basket. With the help of another, she picks the basket up and places it atop her head, allowing her to carry it outside. The warm sunshine and fresh air greet Emara again, making her smile. She walks toward the laundry area as her mind wanders.

I think I need to spend some more time with my brothers before leaving on the Journey. I need to learn how to defend myself better. I need to spend some time with Selina. What am I going to take with me on the Journey?

"Emara, let me help you," breaks into her thoughts. Emara looks up at an older woman who grabs the basket, helping bring it to the ground.

"Thank you. Mother said to bring this to you."

"Of course. There is always laundry to be cleaned. I am

glad your father arrived in time to save you and Enon from those horrible men. How are you feeling?"

"I'm well."

"I'm glad to see your face is mending. I've some clean laundry that needs to be taken back. Do you think you can manage alone?" The kind woman shows Emara the group of baskets that have folded linen in them.

"Yes, if you don't mind multiple trips."

The older woman chuckles as she pats Emara's back. "Of course not. It'll allow you more time outside." Emara takes a breath, and the woman loads her head with the first basket. Once the basket is on Emara's head, the woman returns to the dirty laundry in the basket, making quick work of sorting and assigning it to the others who are assisting her. The woman looks up, finding Emara still standing there. "Emara, is everything all right?"

Emara blushes at being caught staring. "Yes, I'm just amazed at how efficient you are."

"You're kind. I like doing laundry, and I've been doing it a long time. Run along, my lady."

Emara smiles back at the woman, then turns away. On one of her trips to the infirmary to deliver clean laundry, a group of giggling children race by, playing a game of tag that nearly topples the basket of clothing off her head.

A little girl stops and looks at Emara. "Can you play with us?"

"I would very much like to, but I can't today."

The little girl nods her head and continues playing.

Emara watches the children for a minute until they disappear around a corner and sighs. When she arrives at the infirmary, a woman takes the dirty basket she brought back with her, depositing it to be filled again, while another helps

Emara remove the basket of clean linen from her head. Emara works putting the last load of clean laundry away.

Once the last of the clothing and supplies are put away, she hears "well done" behind her, and she turns with a smile on her face to find Suyana looking somber. "It is time for us to go to the Stand."

Emara nods, adjusting her mood. A small group of women stay to care for the injured and their family, but everyone else leaves to go to the Stand.

On the way to the Stand, Suyana grabs Emara's arm. "Emara, from what I understand, there will be around fifty families we need to speak with, and I have to be next to your father. You are the youngest and will be the last person in our family they will talk with. You must stand with your family and converse with them. Understand?"

Gilgal looks at Emara. "Hiding behind your brothers will not work anymore. You are of age."

"You can do it, Emmy."

Telah touches his sister's arm. "I will be next to you and will help where I can."

The king's family arrives at the Stand. There is a line of families and people from the community. The king and his family start the procession. The king hands the family patriarch or widow a healthy young female sheep. "The ewe does not replace your lost family member—none of the gifts given by the community will replace them—but we hope this will help your family move forward." They work down the line of the different families, offering their gratitude for a life well lived and condolences for the family's loss. When the king's family is done with the line of families, it is some time later. They quietly stand until every community member has finished with the line of families.

It is dark when everyone has finished and the family members of the deceased start returning to their homes. The king's family is tired and hungry and returns home without a word. When they reach home, there is a simple meal of different fruits, nuts, jerky, potatoes, corn, and carrots sitting on the family table for them to eat. They eat their cold meal quietly, as no one wants to talk. It has been an ugly week.

PREPARATION

SEVERAL DAYS LATER, SUYANA AND Emara excuse themselves from the dinner table, heading to the infirmary before retiring for the night. They walk quietly arm in arm. "You did a wonderful job the other day. Thank you."

"I was worried that I would say something wrong. I just spoke from the heart."

"You did well." Mother hugs her daughter's shoulder. "It bothers me that you can work in the infirmary without issue, but when it comes to sharing your feelings, you have difficulty. Is there a reason?"

Emara shrugs, looking at the ground in front of her. "I don't know."

When they reach the infirmary, Mother squeezes her daughter's shoulder again. "Something to think about."

SUYANA AND EMARA CONTINUE CARING for the injured day in and day out; finally, the last of the injured disperse to their homes, making it possible for life to resume to normal in the royal household.

This is the first day Emara is free of responsibility and can start preparing for the Journey. First thing she wants to do is go to the precipice. She dresses and goes to the kitchen to pack food.

Suyana smiles at her daughter, turning to share a hug. "What are your plans today?"

"I'm going to get more herbs for the infirmary. The supplies are low, and we may also need some for the Journey. I know where they grow, and I will be back before dinner."

"You are not going alone, Emara. You must take one of your brothers."

"Enon will go with me."

"Have you discussed this with him?" Seeing the look on Emara's face, Suyana walks Emara to the dining room where the men are eating.

Emara stands next to Enon, and he looks up at his sister with a mouth full of food. "The herbs are low in the infirmary. I'm collecting herbs today so . . . would you go with me?"

Her brothers look at Enon as he continues to chew his food.

"Why does it have to be today?" Helam rubs his chin.

"Because the herbs in the infirmary are low."

"Can we do it another day?"

Telah starts, "We were . . ." Hezekiah kicks Telah under the table, letting him know to be quiet.

Suyana touches Enon on the shoulder. "The supplies in the infirmary are critically low, and it would not be good if we ran out of medicine."

Enon looks at his brothers and shrugs, getting up from the table. "I'll go with you. I'll get some horses from the stable."

Suyana gently kisses Enon's forehead before he dashes out the door. Emara heads back to the kitchen with her mother following. "Emara, pack some food for your brother." When Emara finishes packing some added supplies, her mother adds, "The both of you be back before dark."

Emara nods, walking outside with the pack. Enon brings two horses, and Emara joins him, leaving for their outing with Enon's guards shadowing behind them as they leave the gate.

"Why did you shrug your shoulders?"

"We planned to go hunting, and I was looking forward to it." Emara frowns. "There will be many other days for hunting. Since time is limited with my little sister, I prefer spending it with you." Emara looks up, and he says, "Better?"

Emara grins at her brother. "Better."

After leaving the city gates, they quickly travel up the hill toward the forest to find the herbs. A little while later, Emara stops and dismounts. She gets the backpack and starts climbing toward the grouping of trees that is nearby.

Enon hurries to catch up with her. "Why are you in such a hurry?"

"Because I want to go to the precipice. That is what I really want to do today."

Enon laughs. "You're trying to get this done quickly so you can do what you really want to do."

"Yes."

"That precipice is amazing. Before you ask, I'll take care of our guards." He winks at his sister. "Tell me what to do."

"You see this white flowering plant?"

"Yes."

Emara takes hold of the plant, demonstrating what to do. "This is yarrow. Cut it here so that it will grow back, and place what you cut in this cloth. Like this."

"How many do you need?"

"A lot. It's going to take some time."

"What's it used for?"

"It is used to clot and heal wounds." After observing him harvest a couple stems, Emara stands up. "While you're doing that, I will get the cypress cones. Be back shortly.

"Don't go too far, Emara."

Emara starts searching under the trees for the cones she needs. After finding the specific cones, she returns to Enon, who has a pile of cut stems.

"That's good." Emara carefully wraps the cloth around the cut stems. Once the cut stems are packaged in the cloth, she returns the cloth to the backpack. Emara walks to a plant that contains winged leaf stalks, and she shows the leaf to Enon. "Here is the next herb, comfrey, and another cloth. We need the root. It's used in a poultice for arthritis, bruises, burns, and sprains. It is not to eat, and you gather the roots on this plant like this." Enon follows Emara's visual instructions by finding the root and cutting off pieces at the joints of the root. "This is not the best time of the year to do this, but our supplies are so low that we need to obtain more. I'm going to get the next thing we need." Emara goes to a nearby birch tree, scraping the bark and putting it in a pouch. Once done filling the pouch, she returns to Enon.

"These are good. You should have some." Enon tears off a strawberry and pops it in his mouth.

"Yes, they are good. Where are the roots?"

"Over there." Enon nods his head in the direction of the cloth.

Emara walks over to the cloth to find the gathered roots. She drops to the ground, gathering up the roots into the cloth before packing it away in her backpack. She walks back to Enon and sits down beside him. "Are you still hungry?"

"Yes, can we eat?"

Emara pulls off the backpack and pulls out the different cloths containing the collected herbs, empty cloth, and a waterskin before finally pulling out the food. There is leftover slow-roasted marinated venison, corn flatbread, and potato, which they quietly eat for a little while.

"What's next?"

"I have two more items to get near the river . . . but that can be done another day. I got the most important items, so let's finish eating and go to the precipice."

They quickly finish eating their food without further conversation. Once done, Emara packs up everything while Enon grabs a cloth and starts gathering strawberries. They walk back to the horses that are grazing with their guards standing watch.

On their way to the precipice, Enon stops his horse near their destination and allows the guards to validate that the area is safe. "Emara and I brought you a treat to eat while you wait for us here." He reveals the strawberries to their shadows. They eye the sweet treat and nod in understanding. "Good. We will be back to pick you up before dark."

Their mounts are tired and are happy to rest with the men. They leave the guards with their strawberries and horses, continuing toward their destination. Before too long, they arrive at the base of the precipice, away from the guards' view.

After a brief climb they arrive at the top of the precipice, breathing deeply from their exertion and grinning from ear to ear. Emara takes off the waterskin and proceeds to take a drink. Once done, she hands the waterskin to Enon, who also quenches his thirst. They sit on the precipice, looking out over the edge while the sun shines down and the stone warms them.

After a time, Emara breaks the silence. "I've decided to

take the Challenge, and I hope you are still willing to be my guardian."

"I'll be your guardian. You know what this means, don't you?"

"Yes. I'd rather take my chances outside the city for a year than be joined. Enon, I need you to teach me those moves that you used in the market so that I am better able to defend myself."

"I'll teach you before you leave for the Journey."

"Thanks, Enon. Next step—telling Mother and Father. They won't be pleased."

"I agree. But if you really want this, then you'll have to stand your ground." Enon looks up at the sky. "We need to go."

Emara searches through her pocket for another cloth. "We can't go home without this item." Emara pulls out a cloth and a little pouch, which she waves. "Found it." She quickly jumps to her feet. "Here." She shoves the cloth Enon's way. "You hold the cloth while I scrape. Hold it open right here."

Once Enon is in place, she takes the knife and scrapes the lichen from the rock face. After gathering the dust in the cloth, she transfers it to the small pouch. She closes the pouch and puts everything back in her pocket except the knife, which she returns to its sheath at her waist.

"Beat you to the bottom." Emara drops quickly over the edge, disappearing from view. Grinning, Enon starts his own descent. When Enon arrives on the ground, Emara grins at him and they both silently head toward their horses and guards. Arriving at their destination, the guards hand their horses to them, and they both mount up and head home with their shadows following behind.

ANNOUNCEMENT

THEY ARRIVE HOME—LATE. ENON AND Emara make sure
their horses are cared for before heading to the dining room.
Suyana greets them with a warm hug and bids Emara and
Enon to hurry and wash up. Enon and Emara return to the
table where the family is gathered. They sit, looking to see
what is left on the table to eat, finding there is grilled squirrel,
corn flatbread, cut potatoes and carrots mixed with onion,
tomato, and chiltepin salsa, and a paw-paw dessert. The smell
of the delicious food lingers in the air, making their mouths
water and their stomachs growl. There is enough food left to
fill their plates.

Once they have food on their plates and have taken a
couple bites of food, Gilgal looks at them. "How was your
trip today?"

"Fine."

"Did you find the herbs?"

"Most of them, but I will have to take another trip to
finish up. I will show you what I collected after dinner."

Suyana nods. "The Journey is less than two weeks away, Emara. It is time we make preparations."

Emara swallows the food in her mouth. "Yes, it is. I've decided to take the Challenge." She shovels more food in her mouth. Everyone stops and looks at Emara while Enon continues eating without looking up.

Telah throws his spoon onto the table and pounds his fists. "My sister must be of simple mind." Emara jumps. "Couldn't you have waited until after the Journey to make this decision? I don't want you to go, so this must be some kind of joke. You can't do this. I won't let you." He gets up from the table, leaving the room.

Suyana looks to Gilgal. He slightly shakes his head, placing a hand on Suyana's arm and gently squeezes. Her mouth closes, and Gilgal turns to Emara. "Emara, have you thought this out thoroughly?"

Enon looks at his father. "She has been thinking about this for weeks."

"I asked Emara. Not you."

Emara swallows. "Yes, I have."

Suyana touches Emara's arm. "You know what this means?"

"It means I will have to leave by sunrise the day after we return to Uthal. It means I will not be able to return to the city for a year. It means I may not return at all depending on what happens to me outside the city."

"But why the Challenge?"

"I'm not ready to be joined to a husband. I need time to grow up—to find myself. I need to know what I want to do with my life. I don't want you telling me who to join. I'm definitely *not* ready for a husband. I would not be happy, so the other option available to me is the Challenge."

Suyana and Gilgal look at one another.

Hezekiah sits back in his chair. "Who's going to be your guardian?"

Emara looks at Enon, then turns to Hezekiah. "Enon."

"Did Enon have any say in your decision?"

"No, he did not. I did it all on my own."

The room is quiet again until Suyana questions. "But what about—"

As quick as a knife cuts thread, Gilgal turns to Suyana and soothingly states, "She has until after the Journey before it is announced." Looking at his children, he says, "I guess that is it. All we truly want is for each of you to make your own decision and then live with the consequences of that decision."

Suyana takes Gilgal's hand while taking a fortifying breath. "I also agree with your father." Looking at each one of the children left in the room, she says, "We desire your happiness and welfare above all else." Turning to Emara, she says, "I am going to miss you terribly when the time comes. At least we have the Journey to be together." Suyana sighs. "I knew you would be leaving home one day, but not like this." She gets up from the table. "I am going to check on Telah."

Helam leans forward in his chair. "Before you go, Mother, I have something to say." Suyana looks at Helam, who has been quiet throughout Emara's announcement. Seeing his resolute face, she sits down.

"Do you truly speak the truth when you say you only desire our happiness and welfare?"

"Yes."

"If that is the case, I do not wish to be joined to the woman my parents have arranged for me. If you truly care about my happiness, I want to be joined with Selina. I love her, and she is an asset in my life. I do not care to be joined to another."

Helam's parents look at each other. Gilgal puts his hands on the table. "You have already postponed the Joining several years. Do you realize that by not accepting her, you may thrust this city into war?"

Helam eyes his father and talks above his siblings' comprehension so that only his parents understand. "Father, look at it this way: the first offense has already taken place, even if it was intended for a positive purpose. Based upon what was said earlier, that has yet to be seen. I feel we can talk our way out of the arrangement due to his decision and all will turn out well in the end. After all, the alliance between both cities remains positive."

Gilgal rubs his chin looking at his son. "This will require gifts."

"I am willing to provide them."

"Are you sure you want to do this?"

"I am sure."

Suyana looks at her husband. "She will make a good queen."

Emara smiling, "I know Selina loves Helam with all her heart. Please allow Helam and Selina to be bound."

Enon looks at Helam and then at Gilgal. "Selina always helps Helam move in a positive direction. From watching you, Father, being king is difficult enough with someone you love. Why would you have Helam be king with someone he doesn't love?"

Hezekiah leans forward and puts his hands on the table, imitating his father. "She is the prettiest girl in the city. Think how beautiful your grandchildren will be."

The table is quiet and all eyes are on Gilgal. He sighs.

"You have all made valid points. Helam, since you are willing to deal with the consequences, you may be joined to Selina. A roar goes up from the children, making Suyana and Gilgal smile.

Suyana gives everyone a hug and a kiss. "I am going to find Telah."

Helam looks at Emara. "You're not going to be around for the Joining, and Selina will not be happy. We both want you there."

Standing up, Gilgal continues, "It is getting late. It is time for all of us to go to bed. Helam, we shall talk more tomorrow." On his way out of the room, his children overhear, "My children are growing up."

Everyone in the room gets up and congratulates Helam. "I don't know how that was accomplished. Thank you so much for your input and support. Emara, thank you for paving the way. You have more courage than your big brother." Helam hugs his little sister.

There is so much to be done over the next two weeks. The royal family visits Selina's parents, Lahonti and Abish, and Helam's necklace is accepted by Selina. The decision is made to have the Joining ceremony between Helam and Selina the day the mothers and daughters return from the Journey, which ensures that Emara and Enon will be present.

The mothers work closely together regarding plans for the Journey and for the Joining while the rest of the family are assigned tasks to build, obtain, or pack. Helam needs to make a home for Selina. Father needs to provide food for the Joining. Traveling gear and supplies need to be gathered and packed. All of the family work together to get the jobs done.

One evening around the dinner table, the family discusses their plans. Suyana looks up from her list. "Everything must be planned perfectly before we leave on the Journey. There will be no time when we return to fix anything." Looking at the men around the table, she says, "You must be able to carry out my instructions. This is a big day for Helam and Selina."

Emara pleads, "Mother, I know I need to complete the tasks, but I still need to get the rest of the herbs before we leave. Can you please assign that to me one day soon?"

Enon leans forward, getting his mother's attention. "Emara asks every evening."

"I know. I know. There is so much to be done. Emara, I am writing it down. Enon, thanks for accompanying Emara on her tasks. Are you sure you have your assignments covered?"

"As long as you allow me the early morning hours to get things done, I am happy to accompany Emara. She's been a great help in the morning." Enon winks to Emara, and the brothers grin.

A few days later, Emara is assigned to get the remaining herbs. Enon and Emara head out after the daily morning self-defense lesson with her brothers.

"You're getting better every day."

"Thanks. I really appreciate you instructing me. You're a wonderful teacher."

"There are not many days left before you leave."

"Will I be ready?"

"I think you're getting there, but it is going to take more than a few weeks of training to be proficient. Since we only practice in the morning and because our parents don't know, you can't practice more often."

"I know. But I'm better than I was prior to you teaching me."

"That you are."

TWO DAYS BEFORE THE JOURNEY starts, the family sits around the table. Suyana again dishes out the tasks to be completed the next day. "Emara, your task is to spend the day any way you want, and of course Enon will accompany you."

Emara's face lights up. "Oh. Thank you, Mother." Emara gets up from the table, walks to where her mother sits, and wraps her arms around her.

Suyana pats her daughter's arm. "Spend it wisely, my dear."

ON THIS PARTICULAR SPRING DAY, her last day before the Journey starts, Emara starts the day off with instruction from her brothers by the lake where they have their lessons. Pole in hand, Emara is to fend off her brothers. As her brothers commence their attack, Emara does the best she can to thwart their advances.

"Ow, Emara! Be a bit softer while we practice with you. We want to see you off tomorrow, not be stuck in the infirmary."

"You can use all your power with an enemy." Helam brings his pole down toward Emara. She steps back, allowing the pole to slice the air rather than connecting with her.

"Remember, above all else, keep your calm . . ." Enon's pole connects with the ground right behind Emara.

Telah swings his pole. "So you can out maneuver your enemy." Emara takes a step back to avoid Telah's pole but connects with Enon's pole, which throws her off balance, and she falls to the ground. Her brothers' laugh, and Enon holds out his hand to help her get up.

"One more thing, Emmy. Know what is going on around you so you don't fall." Telah leans on his pole.

Emara grabs Enon's hand, and he helps her to her feet. "Ready to go again?" he asks.

Breathing hard for a little while, Emara grins. When her breathing has settled down enough, she answers Enon with a nod. As they continue training, a little way off there is a pair of blue eyes watching the exchange.

THE STAND

"Emara, it is time to wake up." Gilgal walks into her room. "It is your big day."

Rubbing her eyes, she says, "Right. I'm getting up." She stretches and yawns. "I better get dressed." As she gets out of bed, she winces as her body reminds her of yesterday's extended practice with her brothers.

Gilgal sees his daughter wince as he turns to leave her room and stops. "Are you all right, Emara?"

"I'm fine, Father. I must have slept wrong."

"You have been doing that a lot lately. Is your bed comfortable?"

"It is fine, Father." Emara gives her father a hug. Gilgal returns his daughter's hug with a fierce bear hug, then leaves the room. Closing the door to her room, Emara goes to her clothes to decide what to wear. There is a knock on the door, which causes her to stop and open the door. "Mother. Come in. I need your help. I can't decide what to wear."

"Nervous?"

"Yes!"

"Emara." Suyana waits for her full attention. "Everything is going to be fine. I will be with you. The time for nerves is when you get back, because the following day you will be leaving on the Challenge."

"Thanks, Mother. That really helps."

"I remember when I was your age going on the Journey. I was nervous too."

Suyana looks in Emara's cabinet. There are short-sleeved shirts and long-sleeved shirts. Suyana looks at the short-sleeved shirts in vibrant colors and different textures, from fine twined linen to something more durable made of a mixture of wool and flax. Reaching for an outfit, she says, "how about this one?"

"That one doesn't fit anymore. It's too big."

"It is?" Suyana looks at her daughter closely. "It sounds like you have not been eating enough." She picks another sturdy outfit. "How about this one?"

"I don't know."

"You are going to have to decide, dear."

Emara closes her eyes and grabs a shirt. Opening her eyes, she finds she has picked a sturdy, muted green top with colorful flowers embroidered on the hem. Holding it up in front of her, "Mother, do you think this will be all right?"

"For pulling it out with your eyes closed, it is definitely a great choice. It will accentuate those lovely dark green eyes you have." After rummaging through her skirts, Suyana pulls out a matching skirt. "What about this skirt?"

"It'll work."

Suyana hands the skirt to her daughter. "Now, get dressed and I will meet you in the dining room for breakfast."

When Emara finally enters the dining room, all eyes turn to her. "You are a slow turtle this morning, Emmy."

"Enon," Suyana interrupts, "please get Father, as I need to ask him some questions." Turning to her daughter, she says, "Emara, sit down and eat." Enon grins, getting up from the table to obey Mother's request while Emara does the opposite. A plate of food is set in front of her, and she looks up at her mother. Suyana smiles and winks. "I saved you some food." Emara, smiles a thank you to her mother and starts eating. "There is not much time left, so you need to hurry." While braiding Emara's hair into something more than plain braids, she begins questioning her sons remaining around the table.

"Telah are the horses ready?" Telah shakes his head. "Off with you. Get it done."

Gilgal enters the room and sees all the commotion. He shakes his head. "Mother, settle down. You are nervous. Everything is going to be fine."

"You are right. I am nervous. My only daughter stands before Uthal to start her Journey, and everything needs to be ready."

"I have been told you need me."

"Are you sure you, Lahonti, and the boys can put together the remaining items for the Joining ceremony for Helam and Selina without help from us mothers?"

"We shall do fine. You both have written everything down on parchment—what we need to do and when we need to do it. I am sure that between all of us men, we can put together a beautiful ceremony."

"My blessing is with all of you. Thank you." Suyana gives Gilgal a kiss on the cheek. Enon walks in, hearing the end of the conversation, and Suyana turns to him. "Enon, I know you desire to help with the plans, and you can, but your primary concern right now as Emara's guardian is . . ."

"I know. My main concern is getting everything ready to go on the Challenge. I'm already working on it."

"Good. I am glad you are organized."

Finished with breakfast, Emara quietly gets up and excuses herself to the water room. When she returns, her family is waiting for her.

"Let's go." Gilgal leads the way outside where the guards are waiting. Emara sees that there are three horses, two to ride and one packed with supplies. The entourage of family, horses, and guards walk toward the Stand while the royal family talk among themselves. Arriving at the Stand, there is a throng of people. Gilgal quickly kisses his wife, then departs with Helam and some of the guards, heading toward the stairs to officiate. Suyana and Emara walk over to one side of the Stand where the group of mothers and daughters who are going on the Journey congregate. The twenty-five girls wait to be introduced to the city as this year's newly available women. Emara's remaining brothers take the horses to the other side of the Stand, where the families and gear wait for mothers and daughters. The community stands in front of the Stand with guards interspersed, making sure safety and order is maintained.

Looking around, Emara spots Selina and Abish coming their way. "Selina." Emara greets her with a hug. "It's good to see someone I know who is my own age. Nervous?"

"Yes! You're probably more nervous than I am. I keep reminding myself that when we get back, I'll be joined to Helam." She touches the necklace at her throat, and her face morphs into a frown. "You, on the other hand, will be leaving on the Challenge. How can you do that to me? You know, you could have any man. You're good-looking and a princess."

"Selina, I don't want any man. When I am ready, I want the right man. For the past few weeks you've been trying to get me to change my mind. I've explained over and over again why I'm taking the Challenge. Why can't you accept it?"

"Because I do not want to lose you." Selina pouts. "You are my best friend."

"I know that I may not come back from the Challenge, but there's a chance that I will. You're my best friend as well, but I've got to do this. Anyway, you're getting my brother, and he will keep you busy." Emara's mouth turns into a grin. "Girls. The Stand is beginning. Let's get ready. Emara, stand fast and don't shy away. I know you will do well."

Ushered by their mothers, Emara and Selina are placed on the Stand for the community to see. Emara hears her father speaking, telling of the seasonal Journey taken by the prospective women and their mothers. "This provides the mother and daughter some final time together before the new woman is ready to leave her home." The audience watches the girls as the king introduces each mother and then the daughter. They step forward together. The mother tells a little bit about her daughter and then places a bracelet on her left wrist symbolizing that the girl is now of age for courting. Emara waits patiently as Gilgal works down the line of girls.

Gilgal walks up to Emara, moving her forward. "Now we have someone very special to me. She is Princess Emara, our daughter."

Suyana continues, "Princess Emara has strong qualities of courage, honesty, and humility. Some of you have experienced her skills in the infirmary because she is a very talented healer." While her mother speaks, Emara can do nothing but stand there with a smile plastered on her face. A pair of magnificent blue eyes in the audience catch Emara's attention, connecting the two of them like an invisible piece of taut rope. The eyes look directly at Emara, but she cannot see the face. The person owning the eyes is hidden by the crowd. The eyes study her, searching for something that makes Emara's stomach feel like it contains a bunch of butterflies. She lowers her eyes and blushes. When she looks again, the eyes are gone. Suyana, not seeing what is happening to Emara, finishes speaking and places a freshwater pearl bracelet on Emara's left wrist. Reeled back to the moment by her father's requesting last year's remaining single women to the Stand and Suyana's tugging on Emara's elbow to move back, Emara takes a couple steps back.

Three women from last year who chose the Joining come to the Stand without a necklace. As a woman is introduced by the king, she moves forward, stating a few things about herself. When she is done, she steps back, rejoining the line of single women and allowing the next woman to be presented. When all three women have been introduced, King Gilgal concludes with, "Gentlemen, these women have four moons left to find a suitable husband. I suggest that each of you who are contemplating Joining at this time or in the near future who do not have a woman for your home, get to know each of these beautiful women." The king turns to the three women. "Please remain where you are until the mothers and daughters have left Uthal." Turning back to the audience, he says, "Those interested in making an introduction to any of these three women will find them here." Turning his attention to the girls and mothers standing behind the three remaining available women, he says, "Now is the time you girls have been waiting for. It is time to get off the Stand and start your journey to womanhood." As the king states each girl's name, mother and daughter exit the Stand to say their farewell to family and get ready to leave.

Emara is the last to be called. Mother and daughter walk toward the edge of the Stand, where Gilgal and Helam join them as they step down. The royals walk to the horses, where the rest of the family is waiting.

Hezekiah greets Emara with a tease. "I noticed you blushed, Emmy. Did Mother embarrass you?" Without waiting for a response, he gives his little sister a big hug. "I'm going to miss you."

"Have fun, Emmy and Mother. I love you both." Helam gives each a peck on the cheek, then turns, disappearing in the crowd to say goodbye to Selina.

Telah steps up, trying to contain his emotion. "I am going to miss you, Emmy." He gives Emara a kiss on the cheek and a hug, whispering, "I love you." He next goes to his mother, repeating the gesture, and then takes a step back, taking both reins from Enon. Hezekiah moves forward and takes Emara's mare's reins from Telah.

"Emmy, I remember when you were just a baby, and now you are becoming a woman. Everything will be ready upon your return. I cannot believe this is finally happening." He gives Emara and Mother a kiss on the cheek and a big hug. "I love you both." Enon walks back to Emara's horse.

Gilgal steps forward as he blinks away the tears that glisten, and his voice cracks. He clears his throat. "I thought this day would never come, but instead it has come too fast. My little girl is leaving, only to return as a woman." Stroking Emara's cheek he says, "I love you so much. Take care of Mother for me?"

Emara nods. "Love you too, Father." Gilgal smiles and gives her a big bear hug and then turns to Suyana. Emara overhears the private exchange, "My beautiful wife, the mother of my children. I am so proud of you. We have four sons and a beautiful daughter. I love you so much. I am going to miss you and will be lost without you until your return." Clearing his throat again, he says, "The boys and I will get everything done and make you proud. Cherish the time you have with Emara, dear."

"I shall. I know you will do your best with everything. I love you too, my dearest."

Emara watches her parents as they kiss. *If I ever get joined, I desire that sort of relationship.*

"It is time to go."

Gilgal helps his wife mount her horse while Telah holds the reins. Enon helps Emara up on her mare while Hezekiah steadies her mount. Emara, looking for Helam finds him saying his goodbyes to Selina under Abish and Lahonti's scrutiny. Emara grins and brings the family's attention to the exchange.

Under Gilgal's direction, fifty of the hundred guards accompanying the group on the Journey start moving. One by one, each girl and her mother follow. *Here we go.*

REVELATION

AFTER EMARA LEAVES THE CITY, she stops her horse, turning to look back at Uthal to see the remaining fifty guards pass by on foot. She sees the bustling city beyond the gates, recalling her happy childhood that has come to an end. She sighs and takes a deep breath, blowing it out slowly as she turns her mare back toward the receding line of those moving forward on the Journey. She nudges her mount forward to catch up to her mother.

"How are you, dear?"

"Fine. Where are we going?"

"You see those mountains in the distance? Up there."

"Is it all right, Mother, if I catch up to Selina and ride with her?"

"How about we both join Selina and Abish?"

"All right." They urge their horses forward until they reach Selina and Abish, falling into step with their mounts.

"Hi, Emmy. Are you excited? I'm so excited. We haven't had an adventure like this ever since I was put under that horrid woman's care. She didn't let me do anything fun. She was so strict, making me act like a proper woman is supposed to act. It was awful."

"Selina," Abish says, "I'm glad for her help. She turned you into a respectable young lady and prepared you to become a princess and eventually a queen."

Selina frowns at her mother's words. "I don't act any worse than Emara, Mother. In fact, Emara has had a whole bunch of fun that woman would not let me do."

Emara leans toward Selina, whispering, "Thanks. Why don't you drop the subject before I get in trouble?"

Suyana says, "I would like to hear about your adventures, Emara. Will you please enlighten me?"

Emara gulps. "I would rather not, Mother."

"Come on, Emmy. You might as well tell her everything. She can't give you a governess now, and besides, it would be nice to bring everything out in the open."

"Whose side are you on?"

"What did I do? All I said was that it would be nice to clear the air about your escapades. You have nothing to lose. You are taking the Challenge. Besides . . . if you will not tell your mother . . . I will."

"Thanks a lot, Selina." Emara looks around her for someplace to escape to, but there is only the road as they continue forward. For a time, Emara doesn't talk while everyone waits for her response. "Mother, I suggest you brace yourself for some startling facts about your daughter." Both mothers become highly attentive. Emara continues. "Selina and I went up to the cliffs."

"You did what?" Abish almost falls off her horse.

"Emara told you to brace yourself. She hasn't even told you half of our adventures."

"Selina, knowing you are to become part of our family in

the near future, there are times when it is best to keep your mouth closed. This is one of those times. This is between Emara and me." Suyana turns her head toward her daughter. "Emara, come with me." She turns and takes her horse to the back of the line. With her head bowed, Emara submits to the unknown penalty she must soon face as she follows her mother's command. When they reach the end of the line of girls and situate themselves with a bit of space between them and the others, Suyana looks at Emara. "Start at the very beginning."

"Are you sure you want to hear this?" Suyana nods firmly. "All right . . . here it goes . . . you can stop me any time."

Suyana remains quiet.

Emara takes a deep breath. "We went up to the cliffs and explored the caves. We found some bats and snakes. We ate snake for lunch multiple times. We climbed up the side of a mountain and found a precipice where we could see the whole valley. Above us, flying, were eagles gliding on the wind, which is always such a beautiful sight. Once, we took some horses from the stable and went into the forest, where we found a pool of water and went swimming without clothes, which was wonderfully exhilarating. We tied up . . . do you really want to hear more, Mother?"

Suyana's eyes glare fire at her daughter as she firmly nods her head.

Emara gulps. "One time we tied up my brothers. It was so funny watching them hopping about like rabbits trying to catch us. We finally let them loose after they promised not to hurt us and to keep it quiet because we knew you and Father would not be pleased. They were so mad at us for a period of time, but they got over it. On multiple occasions we snuck out at night and followed Helam and Enon around the city and had some great adventures. We were scared to death of being caught, which made it so much fun. Oh, and the plainclothes guards Father used to watch me? I was able to lose them every time." Emara continues telling her mother everything except for one thing—learning to defend herself.

"Camp!" The line of people happily stop.

When Emara and her mother get off their mounts, they discover their muscles are sore. Emara tries to rub the soreness out of her backside. "I'm so sore." Suyana just watches, not saying a word, causing Emara to gulp.

The man in charge beckons all the women to gather round to hear his instructions. "It is actually quite simple," he starts. "Separate into five groups of ten." Once the separation into groups is completed, he continues pointing at a group. "The first group will be in charge of dinner." Turning to the next group, he points to them. "The next group is in charge of cleanup tonight." He points to the third group. "The next group is in charge of feeding and watering the few horses we have. The fourth group is in charge of helping the men set up the tents. The fifth group is in charge of gathering kindling and wood for the fire so we can cook and stay warm. Everyone is in charge of laying out and packing up their bedding, grooming and saddling their own horse if you have one, and seeing to other personal business that you need to take care of. We will rotate daily on what job you have. Know your group. Know your job. If you have questions, ask. Do you understand?"

The company responds in unison. "Yes."

"Good. Let's get to work, since night will be here soon enough." The women separate quickly, starting their tasks. Finally, all is done and dinner is ready.

Dinner is a wonderful hot meal prepared by group one, where Suyana and Emara serve. Suyana, a wonderful cook, oversees the meal preparation using some of the supplies she brought. There is seasoned venison, beans, squash, and corn, which the company quickly eats, filling their empty stomachs. After dinner and cleanup, the mothers and daughters sit around the fires, getting to know each other better. The group of women sing songs and play a fun game of tag around the circle while the men watch from the perimeter. Although Suyana participates, the smile on her face is missing from her eyes, and she has spoken no words to her daughter. Emara is part of the circle but continues to remain quiet and withdrawn. When someone asks a question, she answers in as few words as possible.

It is late when everyone says goodnight and turns toward their tent. Emara walks in the direction of her tent with her head down as she mumbles under her breath, "This is all Selina's fault! Maybe Mother will talk to me tomorrow."

Selina catches up to Emara. "Is your mother still not speaking to you?"

"Yes." Her eyes accuse Selina. "I shouldn't have told her, and it's really all your fault, you know." They walk in silence a few steps before Emara spills out, "I didn't tell her about learning how to defend myself."

"I am so sorry, Emara. I was just trying to help. She takes the time to teach you how to do womanly things, but she never really got to know how independent you really are because when you are together, you act like a princess. I thought it would be nice for the both of you to take this time together to . . . to really get to know one another. Like it's supposed to be."

"Oh, yeah? How would you know?"

"While you were telling your mother about the adventures, Mother and I, for the first time in a long time, had an honest heart-to-heart talk. We are finally getting to know each other as independent people. We have so much

in common, including"—Selina grins—"some of our adventures. I never saw my mother as adventurous. I guess I get it
from her."

"I'm really happy for you. I wish I could have the same."
When they reach Emara's tent, they stop. "Goodnight Selina.
See you tomorrow."

Selina gives Emara a hug. "Emmy, cheer up. Everything
is going to be better tomorrow. Have hope."

"I wish I could agree with you, but my mother's eyes could
burn me to ash." Emara and Selina part ways, and Emara
climbs under her blankets, quickly falling into a deep sleep.

Emara awakens to the sound of banging and shouting.
"Get up. Get up. Time to start a new day. Come on wom-
en, rise and shine. We have a long day ahead of us." Emara
gets up and goes outside the tent, stretching and trying to
work out her sore muscles. The sky above is waking from
its slumber with beautiful hues of pinks and purple in the
distance. The campfire calls to her, and she realizes she is
cold and shivers. She quickly advances to the fire, wincing at
the pain of each step. When she reaches the fire, she begins
warming herself. Looking around, she notices her mother
at another fire talking to Abish. Suyana sees Emara smile
awkwardly at her, and in turn Suyana gives her daughter a
smile—a real smile! Emara starts walking toward her only
to be interrupted by their commanding officer telling all the
women that if they are cold they should grab a blanket and
get their chores done so they can leave. "If you cooked yesterday, you now have to get wood. Get lots of wood, as tonight,
we will only have what is carried. If you got wood yesterday,
you now . . ." until all groups know their assignment. Emara
looks to her mother, wanting to talk with her, but Suyana
motions for her to do as he says, so she goes back to the tent

and grabs her blanket, throwing it around her shoulders and starting to look for wood. *I wish I could talk with my mother.*

Off in the distance on a hill, a horse grazes while a tall, dark-haired man with blue eyes looks on the company of girls and their mothers. His eyes rest on one particular girl with long wavy black hair wrapped in a blanket and picking up dried tree limbs. *There is the one with the green eyes. What a beautiful sight.* He smiles, softening the rugged, tanned features of his face.

FRIENDSHIP

AFTER GATHERING WOOD AND PUTTING away the night's
bedding, Emara makes her way back to the fire to warm her
cold body, thankful that the chores she did helped work out
some of the soreness she was feeling. She looks for her mother and finds her helping the next group get everything ready
for breakfast. Emara smiles as she watches Suyana helping
others while she makes her way over to her mother's side.
"Hello, Mother."

"All done?"

"Yes, they said we have enough wood."

"I would like to speak to you." Giving another woman the
spoon she was holding, Suyana takes Emara's hand and walks
to a fire that has very few people around it.

"You are speaking to me?"

"Yes, I am speaking to you."

Emara gives her mother a relieved hug. "Why? I mean
why are you speaking to me now when last night you were
so upset?"

"Sit down, Emara, and I will explain." Emara follows her mother's instructions and sits down near the fire, but away from others' earshot, while Suyana sits down next to her. "Yesterday I was extremely shocked by your revelation. Something could have happened to you on any one of your adventures, especially without the guards." Suyana sighs. "After you fell asleep, Abish and Selina came and talked with me. They helped me see that being upset is extremely foolish right now. Since I have such a short time with you left, I should use it wisely. They helped me understand that I have not really spent the time I should have with you in getting to know your interests and who you really are as a person. I apologize, Emara. I guess I have not been a very good mother."

"No, Mother! You are a wonderful mother. You've done a wonderful job with all of us. It's I who has failed you. I desire my freedom and I love adventure. You taught me how to be a princess . . . and I just want to remain a carefree little girl. I'm learning fast that with age and understanding comes responsibility." Emara gives her mother half a smile. "Oh, Mother, how I want you to be proud of me."

Suyana puts her arm around Emara. "You are truly a treasure, and I am proud of you. Who else could pull off becoming a master swordsman—or in this case swordswoman—not to mention archer under her parents' noses?"

"You know? How? Selina."

"Not Selina. We have known that for years."

"Are you angry with me?"

"I am not. If I had found out about your other escapades a couple years back, you would have definitely had consequences, one of them being a governess. Now it is different. I was so shocked and upset yesterday knowing that something bad could have happened to you, but I am glad you know how to defend yourself, especially since you plan on taking the Challenge. You are going to need those skills."

"I am?"

"Breakfast. Time to eat."

Suyana gives Emara a hug. "We will continue this conversation later. I'm hungry. Ready to eat?"

Emara nods her head, and both get up, hugging their blankets around them. Hurrying over to the line that is forming, Emara's stomach voices its emptiness, and Suyana chuckles. The line moves quickly as each mother and daughter are handed a bowl of hot corn mush mixed with nuts, dried fruit, and honey. They hurry back to a fire to eat their breakfast around its warmth while the conversation flows freely. When they are done eating, mother and daughter clean their bowls and spoons and ready themselves for travel. Suyana quickly fixes Emara's hair for the day and Emara returns the favor, then they empty out their tent. A short time later, the tents have been packed up and the air has warmed up enough, making it time to continue the Journey.

"Do you need any assistance, Your Highness?" Both Emara and Suyana turn around to see Limhi smiling at them. Last year Emara nursed him briefly in the infirmary.

"Yes, young man, we both could use your help getting on our mounts." At her mother's words, Emara bites her lip in order to keep peace.

"Hello, I'm Limhi. What's your name?"

"I think I had better get on my horse since everyone is waiting on me." Emara allows Limhi to help her onto her mare. Once seated, she nods and looks down her nose at him. "Thank you for your help, Limhi." He looks at her for a moment and leaves.

"Let's go." The company starts moving forward with the men starting to mingle with the girls and their chaperones.

Suyana, Emara, Selina, and Abish ride next to each other. "That was not very nice, Emara."

"Mother, I don't want to get to know him better. I dealt with him in the infirmary, and I am not interested in him. What he's got on his mind is not what I want. I'm sure you want me to be happy."

"I was just hoping you would at least give a man a chance."

Selina grins, impressed by this new side of Emara. "All I know is that Emara definitely told him she's not interested in a manner becoming royalty."

"She sure did." Abish tries to keep a straight face.

"Did you see his face? He didn't know what to say to Emara." Selina laughs. "Poor man. He's kind of cute."

"Selina! You already made your choice."

"Emara," Suyana says, "you need to be nicer. Is that understood?"

"Yes, Mother. What do you want me to say, then?"

"I would like you to be nice, rather than rebuff. If you feel uneasy about a man, stay near the three of us. If he makes an untoward advance, knock him on his backside."

"Mother!"

"I want my daughter's virtue to remain intact. I also want my daughter's happiness."

They continue in silence for a while, listening to Selina and Abish talk among themselves. Suyana finally breaks the silence between them. "I learned a lesson long ago about people, Emara. Treating people nicely, with respect, helps them as well as yourself. They feel good and you feel good. They feel like they are special, and they will think a lot better of you. You feel good because they are happy, and instead of having subjects, you have friends. I hope you understand what I am saying."

"I think I do understand now. It's like the experience in

the market when Enon was taken. If it weren't for the people, things could have gone much worse." Emara sighs. "I'll work on treating others as I would like to be treated."

"Very good, Emara."

"I will go and make things right between Limhi and myself at lunch. Mother?"

"Yes, dear."

"Why do we have the guards?"

"My dear, before you were born, there was a war. A group of people wanted complete and total power over the rest of the people in Uthal. They did not wish our people to have their freedom, but to be subject to their wishes and whims of so-called authority. The majority of the people did not want any part of their plan to take over the throne, which resulted in a division within the city. Although we were the majority, the city suffered much loss. Those wicked people took what they wanted and killed who they wanted. They left destruction and much misery behind them. They were, finally, with the help of many people, banished from our lands. They now live in the forest and mountains, still plundering unwary travelers. That is why I was so upset to hear of your escapades, knowing what might have happened to you."

"Then why do we have the Journey and the Challenge?"

"Although dangerous, it is very rewarding. The Journey provides mothers and daughters an opportunity to know one another better and provides an opportunity to forge a lasting bond of sisterhood between both, which is already starting between us." Suyana smiles at Emara. "Its real purpose is to pass down knowledge from mother to daughter. So far, not a single woman has been lost in the Journey. The Challenge is different, however, since it is so dangerous. The women that take the Challenge are few and far between, and I am thankful for that. While on the Challenge, the guardian teaches skills that men know and helps the woman find her place in this land. The guardian stays with that woman until she relieves her guardian of his duty. Then the guardian is free to return to the city to pursue his own life. The other way a guardian is relieved of his duty is through death. Every guardian that has returned says that his charge is happy and well treated, but others have not returned. We still continue with the Journey and the Challenge because it is still the best way we know to prepare each girl for womanhood and life."

"Do the others know about this, Mother?"

"Yes, they know, and still all of them would rather be on this journey with their daughter."

"How come I never knew about this?"

"We did not want to scare you, but now, I wish we had told you. Perhaps . . . then . . . you would have obeyed your parents better."

They continue to ride silently. While the others converse, Emara thinks about what her mother has told her. *I really did scare my mother with all of my adventures.* Emara works on coming up with a nice solution for dealing with Limhi. After some time, the commander intrudes on her thoughts. "Stop! Time for lunch."

The group stops their horses and proceeds to dismount. The landscape is dry, and there are no trees or lush vegetation. Quickly the group works on their assignments. Water is obtained from a desolate well. Fruit, nuts, and dried venison are passed out to the members of the party to eat.

Emara takes her bowl and goes over to Limhi to eat with him. "Hello, Limhi, may I sit here with you?"

"Go ahead. I'm just leaving."

"No. Please stay."

"Why? So I can be snubbed again?"

"No. That's not the case at all. I . . . I would like to apologize."

Limhi eyes her cautiously. "Oh, really. Be my guest." He points to the ground beside him. "Go ahead and start. This ought to be good."

Emara sits next to him. "Limhi, I'm truly sorry. I didn't know how to say I'm not interested in any sort of relationship other than friendship. I'm new to this, and that's the reason for my rebuff. I hope you will forgive me and that we can be friends." Emara looks up at Limhi.

"You know? You have a lot of nerve . . ." He lets Emara's discomfort spread for a few seconds. "But your apology is sincere." A smile crosses his face. "A person can always use another friend."

Emara's face lights up. "Friends?"

"Friends. By the way, I never got your name, Princess."

Emara laughs, knowing that he knows exactly who she is, but likes his attempt at normalcy. "Emara. Just Emara."

"Can I call you Emara?"

"Yes, of course you can. We are friends."

Emara and Limhi continue to talk among themselves while they eat their lunch. When finished, they clean their bowls for future use.

Their commanding officer hollers again, putting people into motion. "Let's go, ladies, it's time to move." The party moves forward toward the mountain in the distance.

During the rest of the afternoon, Limhi joins Emara's group in conversation for a while as they walk their horses. Emara and Limhi find themselves in front of the others as they continue talking.

"I was a babe when the war occurred. My parents were killed when they tried to defend our home against the Gadianton robbers, and I was left next to my dead parents. A neighbor, hearing my cry, found me and took me into their home. They are good people, and I'm indebted to them.

"What brought you into the military?"

"I joined because I didn't want any other person to have to go through what my parents and I went through. I didn't succeed, though, did I? What with the recent incident in Uthal."

"I am sure your being there helped more than you could possibly know. I didn't even know that type of people existed until then. How sad is that?"

"It sounds like your parents have made sure to protect you, giving you a wonderful childhood."

She laughs. "And my brothers. They have done their fair share of trying to keep me safe."

"That is what brothers are supposed to do."

"How would you know?"

"I have younger siblings. Granted, they are from my adopted family, but I want to protect them."

They continue talking until the interruption occurs. "Camp!" Emara says goodbye to Limhi. Tonight they camp in a barren, arid area where the wood they brought with them is split between the evening and morning use. After chores and food, the company falls quickly to sleep—except for those on guard duty.

Every day Limhi accompanies Emara, and it always ends up that the two of them have intense conversations, holding the reins of their horses while they walk under the watchful eyes of Suyana and Abish.

Selina is on her horse between Suyana and Abish. "Why is it that Limhi won't carry on a conversation like that when I'm around?"

Suyana looks at Selina. "I think it is because he doesn't know what to say around us. He is all business and answers the questions we ask but is fearful of reciprocating the conversation."

"Is that because of our station?"

"Perhaps. He is young."

"He seems very talkative with Emmy."

Abish looks at her daughter. "Maybe he is interested in Emara?"

"It's possible, but she has already told him multiple times that she is not interested in him that way."

The mothers look at Selina and then to each other. The queen's eyes turn to Limhi and Emara, who are walking their horses in front of them laughing. "They can have their conversation and be friends as long as it is just that."

Selina looks at the queen. "What do you have against Limhi? Should I warn Emmy?"

"I have nothing against Limhi. He is a nice young man."

"I don't understand."

Abish looks directly at her daughter. "Leave it be, Selina." Selina looks at her mother and then to Suyana and then back to her mother, finally shrugging her shoulders and dropping the conversation.

Emara and Limhi's relationship grows as they continue to talk with one another throughout the day until they are interrupted by their responsibilities. The scenery around the campground has changed, as the company is now in a forest with a nearby stream. The men start hunting and fishing to provide the dinner meal while the women set up camp. Later there is an assortment of fish, squirrel, bird, and snake to eat. Finally, the meal is prepared and everyone eats silently, as the day's travel has again taken its toll. With food eaten, many women tired from today's travel excuse themselves to go to their tents to sleep, knowing that the morning will arrive too soon.

JOURNEY

AFTER A FEW MORE DAYS, Limhi and Emara are good friends. Limhi has become a part of their small group, enjoying daily conversations with Emara and answering questions from the others. Selina grumbles, "Each day continues in the same unmistakable routine: get up, eat, travel, eat, travel, eat, and sleep. I am so tired of this."

"So am I. On a positive note, we have met new people, making new friends and getting to know other people better." Emara briefly looks at Limhi, who walks next to her.

"Have you seen that within the last couple days, some of the guards have given necklaces to young women?" Abish shares as she walks next to her daughter, who walks on the other side of Emara.

"Yes, I have seen that."

Emara frowns. "Me too. It seems like a very quick decision for something as important as choosing a husband." She shrugs. "Perhaps they knew each other before the Journey."

Selina wrinkles her nose in distaste. "Perhaps. It seems a better choice than having an arranged Joining like Helam."

Abish moves between Selina and Emara, interrupting their conversation. "Girls, either choice can be bad or good. It matters how the couple conducts themselves during the course of the Joining that matters. If both parties listen to their spouse and serve one another, working together, then they will be blessed with happiness. It is when they forget what brought them together in the first place and are selfish that unhappiness seeps in and, if not stopped, will destroy a once happy home."

At their next stop the leader announces, "Tomorrow we reach Arnac, the place of women. Men are not allowed to enter the city, which means the men shall remain outside the walls of the sanctuary in the courtyard while the women are inside. This will be the last night we will be on the road for a time."

A roar goes up from the women. Time around the campfire is spent talking to the men until it grows late, causing mothers and daughters to head for their tents.

"I'm glad we will not have to ride after tomorrow until we go home. I'm looking forward to being clean again."

Suyana laughs. "I feel the same way. We have been traveling for six days, and I hope we can get these clothes clean. They have been through much wear and tear this week."

Both mother and daughter fall asleep quickly.

The next morning, Emara suddenly wakes up, finding everything still except for her mother. It's quiet—too quiet. The hairs on the back of her neck stand up. Emara looks to her mother, who is braiding her hair. "Mother, something isn't right. Do you feel it?"

"No. Stay here and get ready for the day, and I will see you shortly." She steps outside the tent, but Emara follows her mother, not listening to her order while she quickly braids her own hair. Dawn has arrived. The guards are on alert and fires are lit. The air is cool, and Emara shivers as it skims the surface of her skin. Suyana breathes in the morning air, smiling.

"Something isn't right, Mother."

"What's not right? It looks all right."

"I don't know. Something seems . . . wrong."

"Everything seems well to me, dear. The guards are on duty, fires are lit, and breakfast is cooking."

"Yes, I can see that, but where are the birds and insects? Where are the noises from the animals?"

Suyana grabs Emara's arm. "You are right."

A man clears his throat. "Your highnesses, we're gathering the women around the main fire. Please move quickly."

"I am going to find our leader and find out what is going on. You help get the women to the fire." Emara nods her head and starts on her errand. A short while later, things start to happen as one by one the mother and daughter duos gather around the main fire. The guards are attentive to their surroundings, noticing the silence in the air.

Shadows lurk in the trees outside of camp as the ominous silence comes to an end. A chorus of intimidating shouting crescendos from the forest surrounding the camp. Out of the forest charges a wave of men dressed in loincloths, with shaved heads and red and black paint on their faces and bodies. They have weapons raised.

Women start screaming, huddling close together near the fire while the rest, not yet assembled, are running for their lives toward the group. The soldiers quickly move to stop the intruders, but there are too many of them. Emara rapidly looks around, taking in the situation as well as searching for her mother while the guards are trying to ward off the attackers.

Emara's eyes find her mother running toward her with a frightened look, holding a branch and looking behind Emara. Emara turns to see a mean red-faced man advance toward her with a barbaric sword covered in razor-sharp teeth. Emara is frozen as he advances. In the next moment, he drops his sword and covers his face, screaming in horrible pain. Emara hears Selina to the side of her. "Emara, snap out of it! Pick up the sword! Your mother needs your help!"

Emara scoops up the sword that the savage dropped, turning to find her mother facing an assailant as she holds a branch in her hand. Emara rushes to her mother's side, hollering the whole way, getting the foe's attention. Suyana looks at Emara for a second, then moves over to the group of women huddled around the fire to help defend them any way she can.

The savage attacks Emara, but she wards off his blows. Her blade bites, and the attacker drops to the ground like a rag doll. Emara follows after her mother, hoping to help her. Another intruder advances toward Suyana and her stick, moving Emara to quickly intervene, dropping another of the attackers. *Thank you, brothers!* Emara turns to another assailant only to hear someone shout, "Watch out behind you!" Emara glances over her shoulder to see another savage advancing with his sword raised.

Emara starts backing away from both aggressors so she can move both into her line of sight and prepare to defend herself as they grin fiercely at her. Limhi intervenes, drawing the assailant that was initially behind Emara away. The princess watches in horror as Limhi is outmatched and is quickly pierced by the foe's sword, causing him to wilt and drop to the ground. She has no time to go to him since she has to fight.

The other invader slices through the air, connecting with her sword. The evil-faced man who just killed Limhi grins wickedly and starts moving toward her, joining the other attacker. Just then another person steps in, confronting Limhi's murderer. The tall, dark-haired man fights on Uthal's side and doesn't seem affiliated with the raiding party. He stands out significantly from the raiders since he is fully dressed and doesn't have a painted face. Emara finishes the job on the painted man in front of her. She looks around, seeing a few more attackers fighting with the guards as the women, still huddled in a tight group, watch in horror at the scene around them and Suyana still holds her branch.

Another invader advances on Emara, and she shields herself again. She doesn't know how much longer she can defend herself, since she is growing tired, but she continues forward. Without any warning, the next attacker drops to the ground and Emara looks to see what happened. There is a hole in the man's back. Emara looks up to see her mother holding the bloodstained death weapon, white as a sheet but firmly undaunted. The helpful stranger quickly encircles the queen's shoulder with an arm and gently takes the sword out of her hands. He ushers her over to the fire around the group of women and sits her down and says softly, "It is over. Let it out of your system." Suyana starts crying.

Emara looks around her one more time, finding the stranger is right—it is over. The guards start checking the fallen, making sure that the invaders are indeed dead, while Emara drops her sword and rushes over to where Limhi's body lay in the dirt, hoping that Limhi is still alive and able to mend. She reaches him, finding that he is indeed still alive and conscious. Selina soon arrives with the healing bag while Limhi coughs and whispers. "Don't bother. I'm dying."

"No. You're not. I will not let you."

"Emara," Limhi grabs Emara's arm, "Help those who really need it. Not me." Selina is frantically pulling out supplies.

Limhi grins, "I enjoyed our friendship." He coughs again, but this time blood flows out of his mouth. He struggles to breathe, coughing up more and more blood until, finally, the coughing stops and his body stills.

Emara closes her eyes, blocking out the world. "Help the others." When Emara opens her eyes again, Selina is staring at her. Emara forcefully tells her, "Help the others!"

Selina nods, gathering up the healing supplies and leaving to find others that need assistance.

"Goodbye Limhi," Emara says. "I have also enjoyed our friendship." She slowly puts down his hand and gets up to walk to the edge of camp. *Limhi is dead . . . I have killed people . . . I am sick.* Emara vomits on the ground. When she is done retching, she stands erect with her back facing the bloody scene. *Why did this have to happen?* Tears come to her eyes, and she lets them fall freely.

LOSS

EMARA DOESN'T KNOW HOW LONG she stands there silently crying. A deep, soft male voice breaks the silence. "Emmy, it's all over." She looks up and sees the stranger. He has the same blue eyes as the man from the Stand, which rather alarms her.

"How do you know that?"

He looks at her for a moment taking a step forward.

"Don't come near me. I don't know you."

"Emmy, calm down. My name is Ammon. I'm a friend of your parents."

"What gives you the right to use that name?"

"I'm friends with your older brothers."

"Stay away from me. You . . . you allowed Limhi to die." Emara glares at him, ready for an attack.

Suyana, hearing the explosion from her daughter, quickly dries her eyes, grabs a blanket, and rushes over to stand between Emara and Ammon. "Emara, stop this. I do know Ammon, and he is a good man. You have now been introduced. Now, come with me." Suyana wraps the blanket around Emara, guiding her to the fire. Suyana sits down on the ground and tugs on her daughter's hand. "Sit down, Emara." Emara obeys her mother's instructions and lays her head on her mother's lap only to start crying once more.

The man quietly talks to the queen while Emara continues weeping, and Suyana strokes her daughter's hair. "Take care of your daughter, and I will take care of everything else." The queen nods.

Ammon walks over to the women, asking if anyone is missing. After a short time, the answer comes back as no. He nods. "Those of you who can help, follow me." The group separates, some staying by the fire, the others following the stranger. He quickly and efficiently puts them to work with the guards to find the remaining injured and address their needs. Ammon next gets his steed and places it with the other horses, making sure that all the animals are fed and watered.

The sun is high in the sky, and as yet the company still hasn't eaten anything, but something smells good. By this time Emara has ceased crying, and her stomach complains about being empty. Ammon comes up to Suyana and crouches to her level, causing Emara to sit up. "Everything and everyone is now accounted for. Five are dead, and eight are wounded but shall heal. Mothers and daughters are all safe. You were attacked by around seventy-five Gadianton robbers based upon the dead. Lunch is prepared for those who want to eat: beans and corn with some jerky mixed in. It is not much but will satisfy until we get to Arnac. Our enemy should not attack again for a little while, but just in case, the guards are at their posts. We need to get to the city as soon as possible."

Suyana nods. "What happened to our leader? I could not find him earlier today."

"He is dead and was found in the bushes. Omni, as second in command, will be taking over as leader."

"Who are you?" Emara asks.

"I am glad to see that you are getting better, Emmy. Let me reintroduce myself. I'm Ammon. Would you like some food?" At the mention of food, Emara's stomach growls fiercely and he smiles briefly. "I can assume that is a yes." Turning his attention to the queen, "How about you, Your Highness?"

Discovering that her own stomach is starting to complain, Suyana says, "Thank you. I guess I need food as well."

"I will be back shortly." He looks at Emara briefly and stands up, walking where the food is prepared. Before long, he returns with two bowls.

They each take the bowl and spoon offered to them. "Thank you."

"Now that you two are taken care of"—he looks at Emara—"I am going to make sure the guards get some food, after which I will be back."

As Emara and her mother eat in silence, Emara watches Ammon and Omni, the new leader, make sure each of the guards has something to eat. They bring bowls to the guards, stand guard for them while they eat, and then go to the next two guards with two new bowls of hot food.

Emara blinks, realizing she's missing some information. "What happened to the first attacker?"

"Selina threw boiling water on him, and Ammon made sure to end his agony." Suyana watches Emara, noticing that her eyes have not left Ammon except to get another bite of food in her mouth. Mother smiles at her daughter's interest. "You are getting back to normal."

"He puzzles me."

"What do you mean?"

"There is something about him. Why is he here? He comes out of nowhere and helps us. I know he saved my life, but he is now taking charge of everything, and everyone complies with his wishes without question. To top it off, he calls me Emmy. I do not like it, and I don't trust him."

"My dear, that is not a nice thing to say."

Emara angrily looks at her mother. "Why does everyone follow his wishes without questioning him?"

"Because he has proven himself to be on our side in battle. Because he puts others before himself. Because . . ." Mother stops herself before she tells her daughter more.

"Because what?"

"Because he is a friend to Uthal."

Once all the guards have eaten, Ammon returns to the group of women around the fire and makes sure that everyone has full stomachs and their personal needs taken care of, but Emara and Suyana take no notice as they continue their heated whispered conversation between the two of them.

"Mother, he calls me Emmy. Nobody calls me Emmy except my brothers and Selina. Not even you or Father call me Emmy. Neither did Limhi. Then out of nowhere this . . . this man shows up when we need him the most. He takes charge *and* calls me Emmy!"

"So you feel that Ammon has overstepped?"

"Yes."

"He has not. Furthermore, if he had not shown up when he did, you would be dead. And that, my dear, is something I would very much regret."

Ammon interrupts the heated whispering. "Are you both finished?"

Mother looks at Emara. "Yes, we both are."

"As soon as you're ready, we'll ride to Arnac. May I have your bowls?"

"What about the dead?" Emara hands her bowl to Ammon.

"They are coming with us. Arnac has a cemetery where they will be buried."

"How do you know that? I thought it's just for women."

Ammon's eyes narrow for a moment. "It is good to see that you are back to normal, Emmy. You're right. It is just for women, but there is a place outside the inner sanctuary where the men stay that has the cemetery." He stares back, melting Emara's icy stare with the warmth in his blue eyes.

Suyana looks at both of them. "We shall be ready shortly, Ammon."

He nods his head slightly, keeping his eyes on Emara. "As you wish." Without another word he stands up, turning away with the bowls and spoons leaving both women. Emara continues to watch him as he walks away.

"Perhaps I was wrong in saying you are finally a true princess," Suyana says. "You were extremely rude. Have we not had enough fighting around here for one day without you throwing daggers with your eyes at someone just because you do not know them? Is not that being prejudiced? You know it is wrong to prejudge someone. Have I taught you that much?"

"Yes, Mother. You did." Emara frowns and stands up. "It's time for us to go." She holds out her hand to her mother and helps her to her feet. As camp is packed up quickly, she decides to try and explain. "Mother." She isn't sure of her choice of words. "I feel . . . threatened by him, and I don't know why. I guess that is why I am defensive. I'll try to do better."

"You feel threatened, Emara?" Suyana looks at Emara, and her daughter nods. "Perhaps instead of being threatened, you are angry with Ammon because he was not there quick enough to save Limhi from dying."

"Perhaps you are right. I don't know right now."

"In time, dear, things will become clear. Remember, the things you learn, you need to apply." Suyana gives her daughter a quick hug. "Right now, everyone is waiting for us. We better get moving." Emara looks up to see everyone waiting for them by their horses. Ammon helps Suyana and Emara finish loading their horses, and then the two women climb on the back of their steeds.

Emara is handed another horse's rein, which shocks her. She looks at the mount—it contains a blanket-wrapped body. "Why am I given this?"

Ammon looks at Emara, revealing nothing other than kindness. "Emmy, the guards feel that you were the closest person to Limhi."

"Me?"

Suyana puts a hand on her daughter's arm. "If the company has chosen you, then you must ensure his body is buried appropriately so his spirit may cross to be rejoined with his ancestors. When we get back to Uthal, it will also be your responsibility to inform his family."

Emara looks at her mother and looks at the body, bringing tears to her eyes. She looks down, trying to get her emotions under control, then finally looks up at Ammon and nods.

Four others in the company hold the reins of horses carrying the remaining deceased while the horses' owners walk. The company is quiet as Omni, the new chief, leads the company forward. The guards are very aware of their surroundings as they move onward, watching for bandits and ensuring the women are between them at all times. Meanwhile, the women are immersed in their thoughts.

"Mother, Limhi was like another brother. I am going to miss him."

"He was a good man."

"How am I going to find Limhi's family?"

"You don't have to, as they will be at the Stand when we return."

"How am I going to do this?"

"With love." Suyana looks at her daughter. "You will know what to do when the time comes."

"You have so much confidence in me."

"That is because you are my daughter and I know your heart."

The scenery takes hold of Emara's senses. She hears the pounding of a large waterfall in the distance mixed with happy birdsong from the trees surrounding her, while the fresh scent of forest flora invade her nose. She looks up to see the tall trees reaching their branches toward the sky and the sun's rays like long spindly fingers reaching through the trees to touch the flowers that lie among the ferns covering the ground. A smile touches her face at such a beautiful, peaceful place only to be interrupted by a male voice next to her that makes her jump. Turning to look beside her, she sees Ammon on his horse. "What?"

"I said I am glad you like the scenery."

"Oh. How long have you been there?"

"Long enough."

"What is that supposed to mean?"

"Emara, I do not wish to fight with you. I have been talking with your mother and wanted to let you know that around the corner is Arnac." He kicks his horse into a trot and returns to the front of the line, leaving Emara to her feelings.

ARNAC

Emara and Suyana look with great anticipation to see the city of women. As they turn the corner, all Emara can see is a great big wall of vertical tree trunks with a wall of dirt behind them. As they continue forward, Emara notices that the wall is divided by a small gate, then the wall continues and disappears in a cluster of trees. Ammon rides forward to the gate and hollers something toward the top of the wall, then a person at the top waves and disappears from view.

Shortly thereafter, the gate is opened and the company moves quickly toward the safety on the other side of the wall. Emara enters the gate to find it is a tunnel in the wall topped by more tree trunks. As she exits the tunnel, she is blinded by the light for a second, making her blink to clear her vision. She stops her horse and looks around her.

The courtyard is empty of people and is mingled with the natural beauty of the forest. Emara sees a small group of women walking their way from the city. Ammon rides back to Emara and Suyana and invites them to meet the women from Arnac. With Suyana's approval, they ride toward the women walking their way. Ammon stops his horse a few feet away, and mother and daughter follow his lead.

Emara ties the reins of the horse carrying Limhi's body to the saddle and dismounts, then follows Ammon and Suyana as they walk the remaining few feet toward the women who are waiting for them. There is an elderly woman who Emara feels is in charge. She speaks first. "Ammon, it is good to see you again." She smiles. "How is your family?"

"They are well." Looking around, he asks, "Where's Loyola?"

"She will be here shortly. I notice we have guests. They must be the future women accompanied by their mothers?"

"You are right as usual, Calene." Ammon returns, grinning. Then his expression turns. "But there was misfortune, and they need the use of the cemetery to bury five valiant men."

"Gadianton?"

Ammon nods.

"It is done. Who are these two lovely ladies?"

"They are beautiful indeed. This is Queen Suyana, queen of Uthal, and her daughter, Princess Emara."

"You flatter us with your kind words." Queen Suyana bows slightly, showing respect for Calene. "My daughter and I are in your service."

"A queen who is wise. You shall indeed bless your daughter with much knowledge; however, you are not in our service, but it is we who are in your service during your stay here. We have much to do, and the hour is growing late." Turning to Ammon, she says, "You know where to put the men. Your Highness, Princess Emara, please follow me." Calene turns and starts walking while Suyana and Emara look at each other. They decide to follow Calene while the three Arnac women leave the entourage to carry out Calene's orders.

"Ammon! Ammon!" someone yells, causing Emara to turn to see a beautiful woman running toward Ammon. He looks overjoyed to see her as well as she runs into his arms and they embrace. Calene, Suyana, and Emara watch the exchange without being able to hear the conversation.

After a moment, Calene interjects loudly, "Ammon, Loyola, we have much to do. You can both talk later." They look at each other and then walk to the horses.

Ammon shows Loyola Emara's horse and mounts his own steed. Loyola unties the reins of the horse that carries Limhi's body and gives them to Ammon, then mounts Emara's horse and reaches for the reins of Suyana's mare. Together they lead the animals away. When Ammon and Loyola reach the rest of the group that is waiting near the gate, Ammon says something to all of them about men following him and women following Loyola. But due to the distance not all the words carry to Emara, who stands next to Suyana and Calene. Emara watches as the men follow Ammon and ride to a rectangular wooden building on one side of the courtyard. After the men leave, the rest follow Loyola to another rectangular wooden building on the opposite wall that looks identical to the first.

Emara concentrates on following Suyana and Calene, who are now talking openly. After walking through another gate at the other end of the courtyard, the three women enter the city of women. They pass several buildings and arrive at a small structure where the doors open before them. When they enter the house and their eyes adjust, they find a clean room with colorful, ornate paintings hanging on the wall and vibrant rugs on the floor. There is a table with two chairs as well as two women standing nearby.

"This will be your quarters while you stay with us. Through those doors is a bedroom, and the washroom is beyond that.

Here is Alma, and this is Orihah. They will assist you." Alma steps forward and bows slightly as she is introduced. Orihah also steps forward bowing when she is mentioned. "Right now, I would suggest washing yourselves and then Alma and Orihah will take you to the cemetery where we shall bury the dead. I will leave you now." Calene bows slightly to Queen Suyana and leaves the building.

Alma shows them the bedroom that contains two beds, one on each wall. There is an archway leading to the bathing room. The room contains a large natural spring that is filled with steaming water. Emara turns to Orihah. "Where does the hot water come from?"

"It comes from the earth and is called a hot spring. You will like it." Alma and Orihah help mother and daughter remove their dirty clothing, then the royals walk into the water.

"Ahhh." Mother moves deeper into the warm water. "I forgot about this."

Emara tentatively moves forward. "Oh, it is so warm."

Alma and Orihah pick up the dirty laundry, leaving the room so mother and daughter may bathe in private. They discover that the water is deep enough to cover them up to their necks. Suyana and Emara use the supply of soap and oils next to the pool of water to quickly clean themselves as they prepare for the burial.

Once done bathing and using the towels supplied to dry off, they find simple white linen dresses with white embroidery laid out on the beds for them to use. Once they are dressed, Alma and Orihah enter the room to help mother and daughter quickly fix their hair. When hair is combed and braided, Alma takes Suyana and Emara to the cemetery while Orihah stays behind to clean up.

At the cemetery, every man is clean except for those digging the graves. Calene is talking with the men around her.

Suyana and Emara are delivered to Calene. "It is time." She lifts her arm and lowers it. Two by two, clean mothers and daughters dressed in a simple white dresses enter the area with wide eyes.

When all the women have arrived at the cemetery, some horns are blown, which startles many women in the group, including Emara. The melodious vibrations resonate throughout the cemetery as the Arnac women show themselves around the perimeter. Emara takes her eyes off the women who have gathered and looks back at the graves that are being dug only to find that the task is finished and the bodies of the dead lie beside the graves wrapped in white sheets. The personal items of each soldier are in his grave to help him on his journey to the afterlife.

Omni goes to the first of the dead, looking at his face and announcing his name. It is time for his appointed spokesperson to step forward to say something about the deceased. As each name is called, a guard steps forward to tell about his friend. Every now and again, someone in the company sniffles or cries. Omni calls Limhi's name, and it hits Emara that it is her turn to step forward to speak for Limhi. Suyana nudges her in the back to move forward.

Emara swallows and out of duty for her friend steps forward. The tears flow freely, but she manages to keep control of her voice. "Limhi was an orphan from the war, and when he grew up, he joined the military to protect the people of Uthal from those who want to rule unjustly, like he couldn't do for his parents as a babe. This was his first assignment as a guard for the Journey, and he felt honored to be given this assignment. His adopted family took him in, and he became an older brother to four siblings that he dearly loved. Limhi was kind, patient, and helpful, and he felt things deeply, but he was also willing to forgive others' shortcomings quickly.

He wanted a better life for those around him, especially for his siblings. I shall always consider him as one of my brothers and a true friend." As Limhi is the last person to be buried and Emara the last to speak, the honor to start the Song of the Dead falls to her. The song helps the deceased find their way to their ancestors, and Emara has never been the one to start it, but today she does.

> Loved ones you leave, Will miss you so.
> Remembered in our hearts, Through life we go.
> Life does not end, Life does go on.
> Follow the path, To return to the Son.
> Loved ones you greet, That have gone before.
> With open arms, To return once more.
> One day we too, Will take this path.
> To return to your arms, At long last.

Everyone joins in the song. Emara sings with her whole heart, knowing she is saying goodbye to Limhi until they meet again beyond this life. When the song is over, Emara steps back and her mother puts a comforting arm around her waist.

The light hides her face, covering the land in a purple hue. Calene takes a breath. "This has been a beautiful burial. I have heard that some of you have felt that you have met your husband and now feel great loss with their departure. Hearts that are broken now in time shall mend. Keep their memory in your heart because death is not an end, but a beginning. One day you shall see each other again and be reunited, and now is the time to look ahead to the future. Daughters, take this time in Arnac and spend it with your mother. Mothers, while you are here, take this time to spend with your daughter. Allow your hearts to heal."

Calene turns and walks by the graves while every person follows in single file, saying a final goodbye. Calene enters a large building nearby and continues walking. Upon Emara entering the building, she moves out of the way and stops to look around.

"It is beautiful. Is it not?" a deep voice whispers into Emara's ear, making her jump. She feels the heat radiating from Ammon as he stands close behind her. If she leans back just a little bit, her back will touch his chest. The thought makes her stomach somersault, so she turns her attention to the room before her.

It is a large and spacious room with colorful murals of natural scenery on the walls, giving the hall a garden-like appearance. Many beautifully ornate carved tables and benches are located in rows at the center of the room. Those entering the room fill the benches. Between the tables are carved vertical floor sconces that hold oil and lit wicks that illuminate the tables and room around them. At the other end of the room is a row of perpendicular tables that contain three ornately carved chairs and a number of simple chairs, making it the head table.

Emara swallows. "Yes, it is."

"You have a beautiful voice."

"Thank you." Her stomach flips again. This time Emara starts walking to escape how this man makes her feel, hurrying to catch up to the receding figure of her mother, who continued to follow Calene.

When she catches up to Queen Suyana, she hears, "Your Highness, Princess Emara, please accompany me to Calene's table, where you shall sit." Emara jumps again, not expecting Ammon to have followed her.

Suyana looks at Ammon, "Thank you, Ammon, as I was

not sure where we needed to sit." The queen takes Ammon's offered arm. Ammon offers the other arm to Emara.

"I will follow you."

Ammon looks at Emara for a moment. "As you wish." Emara frowns at Ammon's back as she follows the receding figures in front of her. On her way, Emara notices that all the other girls Emara's age and their mothers are also being brought by a guard to the head table to be seated. Suyana and Ammon arrive at the head table, where Ammon sits Queen Suyana next to Calene. Then Ammon pulls out a chair for Emara to sit next to her mother. She sits in the offered chair, but to her surprise Ammon plants himself in the chair next to her. Emara looks around for Selina while her stomach somersaults again.

Emara relaxes a little when Selina and Abish sit across from her. "I am glad to see you. Where have you been?"

"After the funeral, we followed the procession into the hall where people were taking seats, so we took a seat too. A little while later a guard came and got us, stating he would take us to our correct seat, so here we are. I enjoyed your singing, Emara. You have such a beautiful voice, and I wish you would sing more often."

Overhearing the exchange, Ammon leans forward. "She does have a beautiful voice. I'm glad you told her to sing more often."

Once everyone has been seated, Calene raises an arm interrupting conversation. When the room is quiet, she begins. "Women and men, thank you for your orderly manner in seating yourselves. It is very much appreciated. This is the last night you, women, will see these men who have accompanied you until it is time to leave Arnac. Mothers and daughters, there will be an orientation in the morning, but for now it is time to eat and enjoy yourselves."

Music starts to play and some other women bring platters of food to the tables along with pitchers of water. On one side of the room is a group of women with an assortment of drums, rattles, flutes, whistles, and shell instruments playing upbeat music. The food set on the table contains beans, corn, potatoes, carrots, squash, and seasoned venison. Corn flatbread and salsa complete the meal. Emara's stomach growls loudly as she smells the food, reminding her that she is hungry. Selina giggles and Emara frowns, but Ammon doesn't react to her stomach sounds, as he realizes he is also hungry. All start filling their plates and cups and begin eating while conversing. Lively music continues to enhance their meal from the small group at the side of the room.

"Are you enjoying yourself, Emmy?"

"Why do you keep calling me Emmy when I haven't given you permission?"

"Isn't it what your brothers call you?"

"Yes."

"That is what I'm going to call you. Are you enjoying yourself, Emmy?"

Emara turns and looks at him. "You're very annoying."

Ammon stops with a bite of food midair in his hand. Turning to Emara, he smiles proudly, "Yes, I am. Are you enjoying yourself?"

"I was until we started this conversation."

Loyola shows up, interrupting. "Ammon, I need to speak with you. It's urgent."

"Can it wait until later?"

"No, it cannot. I need to speak with you now."

"You'd better go, Ammon, it sounds serious."

He looks at Emara for a moment, nods, and leaves with Loyola. Emara watches as they walk away from everyone to the edge of the room, where they talk for a little while.

Ammon's face turns grim and he asks several questions. Loyola answers, then Ammon finally nods and both walk to Calene. Emara continues watching while she eats, and she overhears Calene's response to them.

"Loyola, stay here with Emara. You two," she says to Ammon and Suyana, "come with me." Calene gets up and starts walking away.

Ammon moves over to Emara and dips down to her level, getting her attention. "I must go, but before I do, I want you to have this." Ammon picks up Emara's hand, dropping something in it, then closes her hand over it. "I have to leave."

Emara studies Ammon's grim face. "What's going on?"

"I have to return home. Calene will tell you, but I must leave now." Ammon releases the hand containing the gift, strokes Emara's cheek briefly, then turns, rushing to catch up to Queen Suyana and Calene.

Emara sits there looking at the door where the three have just exited. She looks down at her hand, finding that she is holding a necklace—Ammon's necklace. "What just happened?"

NEWS

LOYOLA BREAKS INTO HER CONFUSION. "Emara, let's leave. Come with me." Emara nods her head and follows after Loyola to the corner in the room where there is a discreetly hidden door. Loyola walks through and Emara follows.

Emara finds herself in a well-manicured garden lit by lamps. On the sides of the path are different rows of plants strategically placed to be aesthetically pleasing in raised beds mixed into the landscape. Other plants that don't need as much sunlight are underneath. The herbal and edible plants are healthy—many with fragrant flowers. Loyola closes the door behind Emara and motions for Emara to continue to follow her. The aroma of the blossoms touches Emara's nose with a sweet array of fragrances, and she inhales deeply, trying to steady herself. Loyola grabs a lantern and continues deeper into the garden, then stops at a small waterfall that cascades into a moonlit pool of water where moonbeams dance magically upon its surface. She invites Emara to sit on the grass under the tree that overlooks the water. Emara sits, allowing the soothing rhythm of the waterfall and the magical environment to calm her troubled spirit.

After a little while gazing upon the scenery before her, she looks at Loyola. "What's going on, and why did he do that?"

"I would like to talk to you about it. I really would, but Ammon made me promise not to tell you until tomorrow when everyone else is notified."

"Then why bring me out here?"

"You looked like you needed an escape."

"Was it that obvious?"

"Yes."

"It's pretty out here."

"It's my favorite place to come . . . especially when something is bothering me."

"You're scaring me."

"I'm sorry. I like you."

"You just met me."

"I've heard a lot about you."

"From who?"

"Ammon."

"I wouldn't believe anything he told you, since I just met him today. How do you know Ammon so well?"

"We grew up together. He's wonderful and I love him a lot." Loyola sniffs.

"Wait a second. I'm confused. You love Ammon? "

"Yes, I do."

"If you desire him for your husband, shouldn't this necklace be given to you?" She offers the necklace she still holds to Loyola.

"No." Loyola laughs and sniffs. "I do not."

"Why?"

"Because he loves you." Loyola pushes the hand holding

the necklace back toward Emara and sees her eyes nearly pop out and her mouth drop open. "Listen carefully, Emara. My brother loves you."

"Ammon is your brother?"

Loyola chuckles again, "This day must have been crazy for you. We were never properly introduced, and yes, Ammon is my brother." Loyola wipes away the tears from her face.

"He told you he loves me? I just met the man."

"No, not exactly. He didn't tell me with words—just actions." Loyola touches the hand that contains Ammon's necklace.

"Oh! But I just met the man!" Emara mouths softly, as she's still trying to comprehend the turn of events. After a little time for it all to sink in, Emara looks at Loyola. "Would you please tell me when I will see him again to give this back?" She holds out the necklace in her hand.

Loyola looks past Emara's shoulder, seeing a person motioning to her. "Emara, I'm sorry. I'm needed now. We'll have time to talk while you are in Arnac, and I'll tell you everything I know about Ammon. I'll see you tomorrow. Stay here and I'll send someone to help you get back to your room." Loyola gets up and walks away, meeting someone in the distance. They talk for a moment, turn, and disappear into the darkness of the garden. Emara turns back toward the waterfall, soaking in the soothing sound and sight again. She puts the necklace in her pocket and grabs her braid and fiddles with the end of it. She realizes she is tired and lies down on the grass, looking up at the sky, seeing the stars dot the heavens and the moon display her majestic beauty upon this garden. Holding her braid, Emara closes her eyes.

EMARA FEELS A WEIGHT ON her shoulder and hears a voice. "Is that you, Emara?"

Emara sits, opening her eyes to see Orihah. "Do you know what is happening?"

"What's happening?"

"I guess you don't know, so we'll find out tomorrow."

"I was told to come and get you."

"I'm tired. Can you take me back to my room?"

"Of course." Orihah leads the way.

Upon entering her room, Emara finds the room devoid of her mother. "Thank you, Orihah." She notices that their possessions have been unpacked.

Orihah pulls out a nightdress and lays it on the bed. "I shall be in the other room if you need anything throughout the night. Queen Suyana is still with Calene. You should go to bed. You do look tired."

"Thank you, Orihah." Emara watches Orihah leave the room. After Orihah is gone, Emara pulls out the necklace, looking at it in her hand for a time and quietly deciding what to do with it. She puts the necklace with her things, intending to return it to its owner the next time she sees him. Emara rapidly changes into the nightdress and climbs into the bed quickly falling asleep.

"EMARA, WAKE UP," PIERCES EMARA's dream, making it disappear. A hand is shaking her arm. Emara opens her eyes to see Orihah standing over her. "Emara, you need to wake up and get dressed. Breakfast is ready and is getting cold."

"Where is my mother?" Emara rubs her eyes.

"She hasn't been here all night, and I assume she is still with Calene. Hurry and get dressed, eat, and then we will search for her." Orihah departs the room, leaving Emara to dress herself. Emara sits there for a minute absorbing everything and sees the clothes placed on Suyana's bed for her to wear today. "All right, it's time to get dressed."

Emara quickly dresses and walks into the main room. "She hasn't been here all night?" Orihah nods, then Emara sees the table laden with food. Emara grabs some sweet bread and takes a bite while trying to pull her hair back out of her face.

"Sit down and I will do your hair while you eat." Taking another bite of the bread, Emara reaches over to grab some nuts, then pops them into her mouth and sits down. Orihah starts brushing her hair while she continues eating. Suyana walks into the room looking tired with dark circles under her eyes. Emara puts down the rest of the sweet bread, unable to talk because of the large bite in her mouth, then walks over to help her mother sit down in a chair as she continues chewing.

"How did you sleep last night?"

Emara swallows. "Fine, Mother. I see that you didn't get any sleep, or very little." Emara pours her mother a cup of cold water and hands it to her. She then pours one for herself, and they both take a drink.

"Very perceptive of you, since I did not sleep last night."

"What kept you awake?"

"You will find out soon enough. Finish your breakfast, then we will go over to the building where we were last night."

"Have you eaten?"

"Yes, and thank you for asking."

"Anything I can get you or do for you?"

"No, dear." Suyana pats Emara's hand. "Just eat your breakfast so we can go."

Emara's concern for her mother supersedes her appetite, but she forces more food down her throat while watching her mother's eyes finally close. Emara motions to Orihah to be quiet. She stops eating and quietly gets up to wash her face and hands. When she returns, the table is clear and Suyana is still asleep. Emara walks to Orihah, "Is there any way we can let her rest?"

"I shall go find out if we can leave her here."

As Orihah turns to leave, Suyana says, "Stop. We shall all go to the meeting together." Her voice vibrates throughout the room, shocking Orihah and Emara. Suyana gets out of the chair and walks over to Orihah and Emara, still looking very tired. Orihah and Emara look at one another, wondering whether to contend or comply with the queen's desire to be at the meeting. But Suyana walks out the door, leaving them to follow.

The three arrive at the building, which is considered the hall, to discover that everyone in the city, including the men, are assembled. Calene and Loyola walk toward them looking just as tired as Suyana.

"We were about to send someone to retrieve you and are glad you are finally here. Come." Calene turns and walks to the head table while Emara, Loyola, and Suyana follow her. Orihah goes to one of the tables where the community of Arnac is seated. When Calene reaches the head table, she waits for Queen Suyana, Loyola, and Emara to find their places. Emara sits across from Selina while Suyana, Calene, and Loyola remain standing. Calene holds up a hand and waits for the room to become quiet. "I am sure that many of you have noticed the men are still in our midst. News came last night that will explain why. We received word that several bands of Gadianton robbers joined forces and attacked Xenu." Calene stops talking as the room erupts.

Queen Suyana bangs a chair against the floor, interrupting the sea of voices. "Everyone, there is more. Please let us finish."

The talking diminishes, so Calene proceeds. "For those of you from Uthal, Xenu is the closest city to Arnac. We do not know if Xenu survived, and we can only hope and pray at this point. Since the robbers have attacked Xenu, it is likely that we will soon be pulled into this war."

Suyana says, "Those of you who have traveled with me here, I want you to know that we sent a rider last night to Uthal to let our people know so they can prepare for the days ahead." The room erupts again in a sea of concerned voices. An obnoxious whistle sounds, and Emara looks toward it to see Loyola standing on the table. The room quiets again.

"Listen up, everyone," Loyola says. "We know this is a lot, but we need you to be quiet and listen until we are finished. Time is not on our side, and they could attack at any time. We need to be prepared, so stay seated until we are done with the instructions." Loyola pauses for a moment, waiting for everyone's attention. "Around the hall are four different walls, and on each wall is a parchment. We have posted a person who can read at each location. You will need to find your name, which will determine your group. We tried to keep mothers and daughters together. If your name is on the parchment, then line up at the door next to it. More instructions will be given to the groups at that time. Men, please remain seated so you can receive your instructions. That is all."

CHANGE

THE NOISE ERUPTS AGAIN AS people get up, talking loudly and looking for their group. Emara sits there digesting everything. *Ammon was the rider. How does he know how to get to Uthal? How does he know my family?* Selina asks Emara something from across the table, but she doesn't see or hear anything, immersed in her own thoughts. Someone touches Emara on the shoulder, and she looks up to find Loyola mouthing, "Come with me." Emara nods and gets up from the chair to follow Loyola, not realizing that she leaves Selina and Abish behind. As she walks with Loyola, she notices her mother and Calene talking.

"I'm glad that Ammon is the rider to warn Uthal."

Loyola stops. "Emara, Ammon is not the rider to your city."

"Where did he go?"

"He rode to Xenu. I hope he makes it safely."

"Why Xenu?"

"It is our home. Our parents, sisters, and extended family are there. He went to help them . . . if he can."

"I'm so sorry, Loyola. I hope he can help them." Emara says with a frown.

Loyola gets close to Emara. "Listen, Emara. You, I, a few other women, and the men you brought with you are the only ones who are trained to fight. I need you to organize this group in front of us."

"What? Oh no. Not me. Why not one of the men?"

"Arnac is not only a school for women but a refuge for some women who have been injured by the outside world, and that is why men are not allowed into the city. They will remain in the courtyard and can venture into the great hall, but that is it. I need you and your skills. I need you to put someone in charge for today, and tomorrow you will lead them."

"I have never taught anyone anything. I've always been the student, Loyola. Perhaps one of the men can teach the women in the courtyard or someone else can lead?"

"The men are not allowed to teach the women even in the courtyard. Your mother has requested you have this assignment, and Calene has agreed. You are trained in how to defend yourself, you know how to read and write, and your mother has confidence in your ability. This is the challenge in front of us in choosing a leader, but the decision is yours to make."

Emara looks at Loyola, digesting the information, then nods.

Loyola ushers Emara forward. "It's time to teach them how to defend themselves. From what I hear, you are well trained." Loyola tells the people at the front of the line to follow them. She goes out the door with Emara following her and takes the group to a large clearing covered in green grass and some boxes. Loyola halts at the boxes, turning to face the women while the group continues forward, stopping within earshot to hear Loyola's words.

"Ladies, Emara is your leader. She will teach you skills that will help keep you alive. This grassy area is where you will train, and behind me in the boxes are weapons. The swords are sharp and need to be cared for because they may save your life one day." Loyola calls six women up to the front. "These women know how to fight, and they are going to help Emara with your training. Right now they are going to get you fitted with weapons, then Emara will tell you what to do next. Find a sword that feels good in your hands and is not too heavy. Please step forward to be fitted with weapons."

While the women start going through the boxes, Loyola pulls Emara to the side. "Emara, Queen Suyana wants to make sure that you have people you know and trust in your group. Selina, Abish, Alma, and Orihah are in your group. You have one hour to get your group in order, at which time Orihah will bring you to the meeting. First order of business is to put together a reporting system in case the Gadianton robbers show up. This parchment contains the schedule for your group. Your group will have first shift at the wall guarding the city, and it starts after breakfast. Any questions?"

"Could you repeat it all again because I didn't quite catch all of it?"

Loyola grins, placing a hand on her arm. "It's all on the parchment I gave you."

Emara glances at the parchment and sees a detailed agenda. "So it is." Emara looks at Loyola again. "Are we going to get through this?"

"I hope so." Loyola gently squeezes Emara's arm. "You are going to do fine with this group, and I'm here to help you succeed. If you have any questions, please speak up." She gives a quick smile and walks away.

Emara takes a deep breath and turns to face the group of women. Most have swords, but she waits until the rest are equipped. Once everyone has received their weapons, she separates them equally among the six women who know how to fight, resulting in each fighter having ten charges. "Some of you I know and some I don't know, but over the next few weeks I hope to know all of you. This has been a lot to take in this morning, and I am sorry about that. We're the first shift to do guard duty, which will start tomorrow morning and repeat every other day. On the days we do not have guard duty, we will have chores and classes. Every day there will be training so we can get prepared—if we must fight, we will be able to do well. I have put you in groups, and the woman I have put you under is your leader and is in charge of your welfare and training. You are to remain as a group, and if there is an issue, she will tell you what to do. Listen to her and she will keep you safe. She will report to me, and I'll report to Loyola. Since we're starting with basics, I find the sling to be the simplest and most useful of weapons. You've been given a sling and a small bag of stones." Emara lifts up a sling and a bag of stones. "It is your responsibility to make sure your bag is full at all times. Small, smooth stones are the best, and similar stones can be found in your bag." Emara takes one out of her bag and shows it to the group. After explaining the type of stone needed, she shows the group how to arm and shoot the sling. "That is what you're going to learn today. Right now, I would like you to find some more stones while I talk with your leaders. Orihah, would you please come with us as well? When your leader calls you, follow their instructions." Emara walks away from the group while her leaders and Orihah follow.

The leaders form a circle. "Is there anything we can use

as a target?" Emara asks. "Not only for the slings but for the rest of the training?"

The group looks at each other.

Orihah says, "I think I know what we can use. Follow me." The group quickly follows Orihah's receding figure as she runs toward a building. Inside they find a stack of long straight poles. Each person grabs one, and Emara grabs a shovel. They return to the field, meeting up with their loot.

"Good job, Orihah. Here is the schedule." Emara reads the parchment to them. "Tomorrow morning we'll have guard duty. Are there any questions or concerns, I need to know about?"

Questions fly. Where are they going to be placed on the wall? How are they going to watch over their group if housed in different buildings? What do they need do while Emara is gone? Who is in charge while Emara is gone? What will they do if the Gadianton robbers attack the city tomorrow while they are on guard duty? What are the classes taught on non-guard duty days? Emara tries to answer the questions given to her. If she doesn't know, she states she will ask and find out.

Orihah touches Emara's elbow, letting her know it is time to leave. "It's time for me to go to the meeting. I'll be back as soon as I can." Emara turns, following Orihah as she leads the way to the meeting.

The meeting is held in the hall where the men are still assembled. Emara arrives to find that everyone is surrounding the main table. She tells Orihah that she thinks she can find her way back, then Emara joins the small group, finding a map of the city laid out on the table.

"The best points to have guards posted around the perimeter of the wall are here." Omni points to different places on the map. "We need horns at each of these places in case there is an attack—they can be used to notify the city. The defensive strategy plan at present is to transfer bees or wasps to pumpkins or gourds, which can then be placed around the perimeter of the wall, and if we're attacked we can throw them at the enemy."

Omni looks to Calene and Queen Suyana for direction. Calene looks back. "Make it so." Each group leader states what they need, their plans, and their concerns, which are similar to the questions Emara wants to bring forward from her group. A big concern for the female group is housing which they discuss at length, and finally agree upon a solution. The meeting ends a few hours later when everything has been resolved and approved.

After the meeting Emara has a chance to ask Loyola a personal concern. "When I was fighting the other day, I got tired even though it was a short fight. How can I prepare myself and my group to be able to endure?"

"That's a good question. When you were practicing with your brothers, what did you use as your weapon?"

"We used poles."

"Poles are lighter than swords. The more they practice using their swords, the stronger they will become."

"Thank you, Loyola."

The queen shows up. "How are you doing?"

"I'm more concerned about you. You both look very tired. When will you get to rest?"

Mother chuckles. "Calene and I will be able to get a few hours of sleep now. I look forward to seeing you after dinner." She gives Emara a hug. "Thank you for being such a wonderful daughter."

Emara nods to Loyola and heads back to the training ground, where she watches for a little while. The long straight poles are posted in the ground in a row, but separated far enough apart to allow each group to practice without interfering with the next group. Emara decides to personally visit each group and sees what she can do to help. The rest of the day is spent with training until it is time for dinner. The groups follow their group leaders to the hall to eat.

Emara starts for the hall with Orihah at her side. "Thank you, Orihah, for your help today. I could not have done this without you."

"I'm not very good with the sling but will continue to try."

"It's your first day, and you will get better with practice."

In the hall they find a buffet-style dinner of beans, corn, squash, and corn flatbread as the base and the leftover deer meat made into succotash. Dried fruit is also available for those who want some. Both Emara and Orihah get some food and find a table to sit at to eat. After eating, Emara takes her dishes to an area for cleaning and finds Loyola nearby.

"Have you received any sleep, Loyola?"

"I will after tonight. There is much to get organized."

"You cannot do everything yourself. You're going to need your strength."

"I'm much younger than Calene or Queen Suyana, so I let them rest because they need it more than I do at the moment. Many of my duties are being delegated, but certain things I must do myself— which brings me here. Let me show you the wall." Loyola takes Emara to the wall and shows her the stairs. They walk the perimeter of wall in the courtyard, and Emara finds a heavy locked door at each end.

"The door on each end separates where men may go, but tomorrow it will be the women who guard while the men make their preparations, as we discussed earlier in the meeting. So the doors will be unlocked and open. Do you know where you will place your guards?"

Emara nods.

"Good. Follow me." They climb down the narrow stairs, traveling to another area behind the hall where Emara is introduced to another set of stairs. Loyola and Emara climb the stairs and walk the perimeter of the wall. Loyola explains the wall, what to look for, and where she would place the guards, which is a little bit different than what Omni shared at the meeting. "If you place your guards here, you will be able to see a greater distance than what the men mentioned on the map." At the other end, there is the sealed door and another staircase. Upon reaching the ground again, they return to the courtyard, where Emara sees men stacking small tree trunks near the gate into the city.

"What is that for?"

"The poles your group took will not withstand sword blows, so the sturdier trunks will replace your poles, allowing them to last longer. I have ordered all the groups to have their own set." Emara sees another group come out from the hall to receive the trunks from the stack to move into the city of women. "The trunks will be up by morning. Do you know your way back to your room?"

"I . . . am not quite sure."

Loyola smiles. "Follow me."

Emara follows next to Loyola, making note of everything around her to help her get her bearings in this small city as things start falling into place.

"Where's Ammon's necklace?"

"It's with my belongings. I'll give it back to him when I see him again. I still don't know why he gave it to me."

"I told you why."

"Yes, but I don't know him, and I'm not accepting any man's necklace unless I want to be joined to him."

"You're telling me your parents have not arranged your Joining?"

"No, not that I am aware. I told my parents that I'm planning to take the Challenge."

"How did they take it?"

"After explaining my reasons, they seemed to accept it."

"Really? My parents arranged my Joining, and I had no say in it."

"I'm sorry."

"Don't be. I grew up accepting it."

"Then why are you here in Arnac?"

"Calene is my aunt. My future husband postponed our Joining, so I took the Challenge, and for the Challenge Ammon brought me to Arnac to help my aunt. Recently, my future husband cancelled our Joining, which is actually a relief, since I'm happy in Arnac."

"When I first met your brother, I was mad at him because he wasn't there fast enough to save my friend." Emara is quiet for a moment. "I'm learning that life doesn't happen according to my plans."

"It doesn't." Loyola smirks. "Life happens based upon the choices we make, the choices others make that impact us, and sometimes, life just happens. All we can control is how we respond. I've learned just to do my best and see what happens."

"Thank you for showing me to my room. I really enjoyed talking with you. I hope that, perhaps, we can talk again soon."

After parting ways with Loyola, Emara finds Orihah, Alma, and her mother in the room. Suyana is busy planning something at the table as Emara comes up behind her mother, giving her a hug while she looks over her shoulder. "You look much better, Mother. What are you planning?" Emara sits in a chair.

"You girls still need to receive your training on how to be a woman." Mother smiles at her. "If you notice on your schedule, there are classes. I am planning those classes and who will teach them."

"Anything I can do to help?"

"No, dear. You need to get some sleep—you have guard duty tomorrow. I am about done here and then will come join you.

"All right, Mother. I'll get ready for bed and then come and check on you." Emara gets up from the table and heads toward the bedroom to find a nightdress laid out on her bed. She grabs the nightdress and goes into the bathing room, getting ready for the night. After a wonderful bath, Emara returns to the front room, where she finds her mother nodding off. She goes over to her. "Mother, it's time for you to retire and get some sleep too. You're falling asleep at the table."

"Perhaps you are right." Suyana sighs, getting up from the table and taking the lantern with her as she follows Emara into the bedroom.

PREPARATION

MORNING ARRIVES WAY TOO SOON for Emara. Mother and daughter quickly dress, then Suyana grabs the parchment off the table and takes it with her. They arrive at the hall in time to get a hearty breakfast, after which Suyana gives Emara a hug, then Emara leaves, heading toward the courtyard to join her group on the wall.

Arriving in the courtyard, she finds her platoon assembled, while the men are busy working hard on their defensive preparations separate from the women. Emara assigns two squads to the front wall, then asks the remaining troops to follow her. As they follow Emara through the gate into Arnac, she shows two more groups the stairs to the wall on one side. After communicating to each leader their positions on the wall, the women follow their leader up the stairs to their post. Emara takes the remaining members to the other set of stairs, explaining to the remaining leaders where they need to be posted, but Emara does not stop continuing up the stairs with them. At each location she explains what to look out for, just as Loyola explained the previous evening, and shows them the horns that were placed on the wall to communicate about an attack. Finally, she lets them know she will be at the front wall with the first two groups. Emara continues around the perimeter until she feels that all four groups are stationed correctly, know what to do, and feel ready for this task.

After returning to the front wall, Emara checks in with the leaders, giving the same instructions. Once everyone is situated, she starts guarding near Selina and Abish. "I have missed seeing you."

Selina looks at Emara briefly, then looks back at the expanse in front of her. "I have missed you too. I thought you forgot about me with your new friend, Loyola. I don't like being brushed aside."

"Brushed aside? What gives you that idea?"

Selina frowns, looking at Emara. "You disappeared from the hall the first night. When I spoke to you yesterday morning, you didn't answer me and then went off with Loyola."

Emara frowns. "I'm so sorry you felt that I had abandoned you. The news arrived that first night and things happened." Emara looks at Selina briefly. "Mother was gone all night."

"Why didn't you tell me in the hall the next morning what was going on before it was announced?"

"You saw I came in with my mother, and before I knew it they announced the attack. I was not aware of what had happened, so I got the news when you did."

"I asked you a question, and you didn't respond."

"I didn't know the news until it was delivered to everyone, and I didn't hear you or else I would have responded. You know me, Selina. You know I would not toss you aside for another person. You are my closest friend." Emara shoots Selina a look.

It is quiet for a little bit while Selina looks at Emara. "And you are mine. I'm scared, Emmy." She looks back over the wall.

"So am I."

"I haven't seen Ammon. He is really good-looking. Where is he?"

"He left the first night. I found out the next day that he went to Xenu." Selina looks at her friend. "Loyola is Ammon's sister."

"Emmy, I'm sorry I was jealous and so wish I hadn't been jealous. What can I do to help?"

"You're doing it. I just needed to talk with you."

Selina walks over to Emara and takes her hand. They stand there, silently supporting each other as they continue looking over the wall.

As the day progresses, Emara sees the preparations the men are making, and an idea starts to formulate in her head. Throughout the day she visits her charges upon the wall, ensuring their well-being. At one of these visits with the leader nearest the gate, Emara starts asking questions.

"Is this the only way into or out of the city?"

Chaya looks at Emara. "Yes."

"Is there a way for people to walk over the tunnel?"

"Yes. Why?"

"Show me please, because I have an idea." Emara falls into step with Chaya, one of her group leaders. Emara learns that she came to Arnac after her husband's untimely death, and Loyola taught her to defend herself. They reach the small room above the tunnel, then Emara investigates her surroundings, especially the floor. "Is there a hole in the floor somewhere, or can we make one?"

"There is a small hole so we can look at who is going

through the tunnel. They are not able to see us." Chaya shows Emara the rectangular hole in the floor.

"This is good. I've an idea for our defense that is not currently being used. I'll take it to Loyola." Chaya nods, and they return to their post.

The day drags by slowly. Selina yawns and turns her head, looking at Emara. "Guarding is boring."

"I'll take boring over an attack." Emara continues pondering her idea as she looks over the expanse in front of her.

"You're thinking about something, so you've got to tell me." Selina gives Emara a sidelong glance. "Your hands are playing with your braid."

Emara looks down at her hands and then gives Selina a sheepish grin. "Yes, I have an idea that I think might work for defending the city. I am trying to work it out in my head."

"What is it?"

"We could drop oil in front of or on our enemy and light it if they ever breach the gates of the city."

"Wow. I never thought you would be that devious."

"We need to protect ourselves from our enemy no matter what. The only problem with my idea is we use trees, and they catch fire."

"That is a problem." They both think about the problem, and sometime later Selina touches Emara's arm. "How about clay? It doesn't catch fire."

"That's an idea I didn't think of."

After Emara's group's day of guarding Arnac, the next platoon takes over and everyone meets in the hall to eat quickly before it's time for practice. Emara sees Loyola, who looks like she got some sleep. Parting with Selina and Abish, Emara walks over to Loyola with a grin on her face and waits for Loyola to finish her conversation with the other person.

When Loyola is available to talk, Emara bursts out, "I have an idea to defend the city."

"You look excited. What is it?"

"The room above the tunnel has one hole in it. Can we make more holes?"

"Perhaps. What's your idea?"

"If the robbers make it into the gate, we could drop oil in front of them through some holes. Then we could light the oil, helping ward off the robbers."

"What about the wood?"

"That was our thought too. We think lining the holes, walls, and ceilings with clay will prevent the wood from catching fire."

"That may work. I will take your idea to Calene, Omni, and your mother to discuss further. How was guard duty?"

"Long. Tiring. And uneventful."

"The best kind." Loyola grins.

After missing dinner to speak with Loyola, Emara leaves to join her group for practice. She arrives to find that the tree trunks have replaced the poles. Her group has already started their practice with the slings.

Selina, seeing Emara, jogs over to her. "I know you missed dinner to speak with Loyola." She pulls a wrapped item from her pocket and hands it to Emara. "Here's a prickly pear— your favorite. I know how your stomach is when it's empty and thought you could use this."

"Thank you for bringing something to eat. It's very thoughtful, which makes me appreciate you even more." Emara deposits it in her pocket.

"It's the least I could do after being upset with you."

"Thanks for being my best friend." Selina smiles and returns to her group.

Emara walks over to the farthest group to talk with them. They stop their sling practice, and several of the women jog over to get the pile of poles that have now been cut in half, carrying them back. Emara asks the next group to join them as well. "You're getting better with the sling but still need to master your aim. Rather than all of us continuing to practice the same thing, and since the poles are stacked here, I thought we could switch it up. Before we start using our swords, we might as well practice with poles to learn the basics. Each of you take a rod from the stack, and your group leader will start teaching you how to use a sword."

Once everyone in their group has a pole, the leader demonstrates how to hold the stick and starts with basic moves. Emara watches the next two groups while their leader gives pointers. Emara continues down the line until daylight fades, then stops the practice and dismisses them to their rooms after a long day. Tomorrow will be training and classes. She has no idea what the classes will entail but will do her best when the time comes.

Orihah walks up to Emara. "Would you like to walk back to the room with me?"

"Thank you for the offer, but I have something to do." Emara smiles at her, and Orihah nods before turning and walking toward their quarters. As Emara watches Orihah depart, her stomach growls, causing her to start moving toward the pond, where she sits down under the tree. She pulls out her knife and the prickly pear, cuts it open, and eats, savoring every bite.

"May I join you?"

Emara looks up while chewing a piece of fruit, then swallows and smiles. "Loyola, I'm sorry if I have invaded your space. I needed some time alone."

"I completely understand. I can go elsewhere."

"No. No. That is not what I meant. Please come and sit with me."

Loyola sits down next to Emara. "It's late."

"Yes, it is, but I can't sleep right now. I'm wondering how your brother and the others at Xenu are doing. When do you think you will hear something?"

Loyola sighs. "Not for a few more days. It's hard not knowing anything."

"I imagine. You stated you are happy at Arnac. Have you always been in charge of its defense?"

"I'm good at it, so I was put in charge of it after I arrived here. My parents trained me to fight, and I'm grateful for that skill. I've also learned many other skills while here at Arnac. Some you will learn during your lessons."

"First day of classes is tomorrow."

"Your mother has put a lot of thought into it."

"I'm sure she has." Emara looks at Loyola. "Do you think Ammon will be all right?"

"He's a strong fighter and is very strategic. I'm sure he will reach Arnac to help them. I've got to have hope until I know otherwise."

"You're a very strong woman. I would be a nervous wreck not knowing what happened to my family."

"Thank you for the compliment, although I don't feel strong. I rather think you are strong since it took a lot of strength to tell your parents you were taking the Challenge. I would never have told my parents, let alone talked them into it, which takes skill."

"Thanks for thinking I'm strong. Right now, I am worried. We are not ready for an attack."

"No, we are not. So our options are to continue to prepare and hope we don't see any Gadianton or live in fear. I prefer to be prepared."

"So would I. Thanks for making me feel better. Mother is probably wondering where I am, so I need to go. I hope we can talk again soon."

THE NEXT DAY DAWNS TOO soon for Emara, but she gets out of bed quickly and dresses. After breakfast, she heads to training, finding her troops already assembled. Today she shows a brief one-on-one combat with Chaya, demonstrating how to use the basic moves taught yesterday. After that, Emara introduces them to the bow and arrows. After the brief demonstration, they separate into three groups, rotating time among the sling, bow and arrow, and sword.

After lunch, Queen Suyana greets the group and leads them to a different room they have not seen before. There are a few women who live in Arnac who teach womanhood classes, and the queen calls these women from the group to stand up front with her. "Even though we are in a time of war, you must still learn the skills of a woman. On the day classes are held, these three women will teach you skills and answer your questions. Mothers and daughters are to work together so you mothers have the opportunity to relay your knowledge to your daughters. Since we are in a time of war, the first skill to be taught is basic healing. Emara, Selina, and Abish will be your patients, since they are already skilled healers." Suyana nods to the women to start their class and steps back. She watches for a little while as her daughter patiently acts as victim for the students. Suyana finally leaves the room, chuckling on her way out.

The next day starts off at the same time—dawn. Today the group is assigned all the household chores for the city. Everyone does their part, including Emara, but she is pulled out of some of those tasks for a few hours for another meeting between Calene, Suyana, Omni, Loyola, and the other group leaders.

The meeting is similar to the previous time as they move forward with their defensive plans. Omni presents Emara's plan to the group. "A few days ago, Emara presented Loyola with a defensive strategy that is quite ingenious. Above the entrance to the city is a small room and within the floor there is an opening. If we create a few more holes in the floor, if the gates are breached, we can pour oil into the holes and light it to create a wall of fire. I have a skilled carpenter who can add the additional holes to make this idea a reality."

"Since the wall is made of wood, how are we going to maintain the wall?" asks one of the group leaders

Omni turns. "Very good question. The walls and floor above the gate will be covered in clay, which will help deter the wood catching fire. We will also use dirt to help control the fire. The opening for the holes will also be lined with some clay to prevent the oil from seeping into the wood."

Calene looks at Emara, then to Suyana, who slightly nods her head, and finally turns to look at Omni. "Make it so."

As the days continue to cycle, the daily grind that started off as difficult becomes easier. The women grow stronger, but sore muscles are something each woman lives with daily. The women use the warm springs to help ease their tired and sore muscles at the end of a long day. Before Emara goes to bed, she spends a moment touching the necklace tucked into her belongings, thinking about the man who gave it to her. She hopes Ammon is safe, for his sister's sake, and that she will have the chance to get to know him better. She wonders why he would give his necklace to a woman he doesn't know and plans to ask him when they see each other again.

On the days when classes are taught, Suyana attends

with Emara, which provides much needed time together as mother and daughter. The queen shares her wisdom with her daughter, and Emara is glad to receive it, learning new skills and enhancing the skills she already knows.

One day Loyola walks in and stands in front of the table where Calene and Suyana sit looking at the map of the city. "The women continue training daily, and their skills are improving as they rotate between archery, sling, and sword. Omni reports that the defensive tasks in the city are mostly completed. I have walked with him, validating that they are in place and ready to use should we need to."

"That is very good. Thank you for your report, Loyola. What do you think of the women's skills?"

"They are improving and still have some way to go, but I think the women can hold their own for a little bit. The defensive plans will give us a fighting chance against an attack."

The warning horns start blaring, and everyone drops what they are doing and heads to the courtyard to assemble. Loyola climbs the wall to find out what has happened while Calene and Suyana stand ready to dispense orders. Emara stands in formation with her company, ready to fight, then the horns become silent. Time passes slowly for those waiting in the courtyard for their assignment, and not a word is spoken as they watch anxiously for any sign of attack from the wall. Finally, the all clear is sounded, and everyone disperses back to their daily tasks.

When Loyola descends the wall, she goes directly to Calene and Suyana while Emara and the other leaders join the group to find out what happened. "It was only a deer that was moving through the forest. I think as each day passes, the anxiety within the city increases."

Suyana exhales. "That makes me feel a little better, but I, too, have noticed the tension building as the days pass."

Calene looks at Suyana. "Indeed it has." Turning back to Loyola, she asks, "Have you heard anything from Ammon?"

"No word has come."

"Keep hope alive. Ammon will be all right." Calene smiles at Loyola.

"It has been a moon, and some word should have come by now."

"You are right, and I have heard other concerns as well. We will meet after lunch."

SUPPLIES

AFTER LUNCH THE LEADERS GATHER in the hall, surrounding the table. Calene stands in front of a different map, listing things on her fingers. "So here are the problems that have been presented to me. It has been over a moon and we have heard nothing about Xenu and have not seen Gadianton robbers—thank goodness. Our food and herb stores are running low. We need wood and flint for more weapons. Have I left anything out?"

Omni looks at the map, locating Xenu. "How many days to Xenu?"

"Two days if there are no problems using this route." Loyola shows the route on the map to Omni.

"Is there a hunting ground on the way to Xenu?"

"Yes, on the other side of the mountain, which is one day's journey from here."

"Do you know the way?"

"I know the way because it's where I come from. We hunt in the hunting grounds and bring the meat back to Arnac. I see where you are going with this." Pointing on the map, she says, "Here are the hunting grounds, and here is where the flint can be found. There is also this forest around us to find the wood and herbs we need, but they take time to gather. It will take us five days to make the round trip if there are no issues, adding one extra day for carrying the food back." Omni nods.

Ituha, one of Loyola's group leaders, raises her hand. "What if Arnac is attacked while you're gone? We're getting better, but we'll not survive an attack if the women have to fight one-on-one. They aren't ready." Ituha has been at Arnac many years and is a quiet person. She does not talk about her past but is exceptionally talented with a sword.

Omni acknowledges Ituha's concern. "We are low in numbers, but I think we have completed some great defensive plans to help combat the difference in our numbers."

Ituha looks back at Omni. "We haven't seen Gadianton in over a moon, but that doesn't mean they aren't out there preparing to attack. How are we going to keep the city safe as well as the group that leaves?"

Kanti, another group leader for Loyola, stands. "We can't stay here and do nothing. We'll run out of food. The garden isn't enough to sustain the city, and we need more meat." Kanti came to Arnac seven years ago and was trained by Ituha, but prefers her time tending the garden.

Suyana, sitting, looks at the group around the table. "We need a plan, and we have to go out of the city and do this. There is not another option."

Calene nods her head and looks at the group. "Does anyone have an idea how to maintain the city and obtain what we need?"

Those around the table are quiet.

After a little time has passed, Emara looks up at the

group. "What if . . . only a small group leaves to obtain the supplies? A mixture of men and women who know how to defend themselves? The majority of people will stay here in the city, continuing the routine, and be here to defend the city if that is required?"

Ituha looks to Calene. "Who would we send?"

Loyola raises her hand. "I'll go because I know the way."

Kanti nods her head. "How many should we send?"

Akna, a third Loyola group leader, pounds her hand on the table. "It must be voluntary." Akna, a tall, stocky, self-sufficient woman, arrived in Arnac after Ituha. She's brash in more ways than just words. She is first to act and is first to state that she does not need a man when she can do it herself, which rubs Omni the wrong way, but he agrees with her work ethic.

Calene nods. "Great points all of you. Women, out of your groups, who are ready for combat?"

Suyana looks to Calene. "Only eight women in each of the four groups are ready for combat per our current calculations."

Akna raises her hand. "Four volunteers from each group?"

Loyola looks to Akna, nodding. "That will give us sixteen women, which I think is a good number."

Omni hits his hand on the table. "I can contribute ten men. They are good at hunting and combat, and some know how to make weapons and how to work flint."

Kanti looks at Omni and then turns to Calene. "The four group leaders need to choose from the volunteers only those who have skills for obtaining the things we need."

"We still need herbs," Ituha says.

"You are right. Out of the women who are prepared for combat, who knows how to find, collect, and work herbs?" Akna looks at the group, and quiet settles around the table.

Suyana breaks the silence by clearing her throat. "There is only one in the city who meets these requirements, and that is my daughter, Emara." She looks at Emara. "Every person must volunteer knowing full well what could possibly happen."

Emara looks at the people around the table, and all eyes are on her, making her uncomfortable. She looks at her mother, then looks at Loyola, finally making a decision, which turns her attention toward Calene. "I will join Loyola."

"Very well. Emara, can someone else take over as leader while you are gone?"

"Yes, Chaya will be able to do it."

"Loyola, do you have someone who can take over your responsibilities?"

"Eida will be able to do it."

Akna raises her hand. "How many horses will be taken?"

Omni looks at Akna. "Since this is a supply party, we'll need all the horses. I know there are not that many, but we will need them to carry food and supplies back so we can return sooner."

Kanti looks at Omni and nods. "It will lengthen the supply we have left."

"Any objections?" The group is quiet. "Then all the horses we have will be sent. How much time do you need to prepare?"

Loyola looks at Calene. "They can find volunteers at their next training."

Emara looks at her mother and then looks at Calene. "I will make a list of the herbs that we need and find out where to search for them."

"If you leave in three days' time, will that provide you enough preparation?" Around the room, heads start nodding. "Good. We have a plan. Tomorrow, we will meet again at the same time, at which point I would like a report regarding who volunteered. If you have volunteered, bring your replacement with you to the next meeting. For the group that is on kitchen duty, please provide a report on how many days' food supply we have left. We may need to start rationing until the supplies have been restored. Make it so."

Emara returns to her group, formulating how to carry out the decisions made by the committee. At their next practice, she stands before the assembly. "A group is being gathered to go outside the city to resupply our dwindling resources. They will also find out what happened to Xenu. I need three volunteers from our group, but they must know how to fight, be willing to go outside the safety of these walls, and know how to hunt for food. In all likelihood, the party may come in contact with the Gadianton robbers. This is a dangerous mission that may"—she swallows—"result in forfeit of life. Please step forward if you would like to be considered."

She makes her choices from those who step forward. "Thank you to all of you who volunteered. You are courageous, but I can only choose three. For those of you not chosen, we still need your courage here to help defend the city. Those who have been chosen, we will meet in the hall after lunch and receive more instructions. Now, those chosen are dismissed to get your affairs in order." The three volunteers leave the group. "To those of you who remain to protect the city, we have great need of your skills. Chaya will take over for me while I'm away. Listen to her, and she will keep you safe." Emara steps to the side, watching Chaya lead. Before long, Emara notices Selina standing next to her.

"Emmy, can we step away and talk?" Emara nods. Selina leads the way, making sure there is plenty of distance between the two of them and the group before turning on Emara. "Are you crazy?"

"No."

"Have you not thought about your poor mother? *You* are her *only* daughter. What if something happens and you are killed? How does your mother feel about this?"

"She doesn't like it."

"Then don't do it!"

"I need to do it."

"*No you don't!*"

"Yes, I do. There's not another person who knows how to fight and knows how to collect herbs. We need more supplies, Selina. I need to do this, and I volunteered to do this."

"I don't want you to go."

"I can tell you don't want me to go." Emara takes Selina's hands. "This must be done, Selina. Mother has accepted this. Why can't you?"

"Because . . . because . . . I don't want you to die." Selina throws off Emara's hands and starts walking away. After a few steps she turns back to Emara. "I want you at my Joining. I know it's selfish. *You* are my best friend"—she sniffs—"and I don't want to lose you."

Emara hugs Selina. "I'll do my best to be at your Joining, but I still need to do this."

"I know." Selina sniffs again and lets go of the embrace. She looks at Emara through tearful eyes. "I still don't like it, and if you don't come back, I am going to kill you."

"Then you better practice." Selina nods, dries her eyes, and gives Emara a half smile, then returns to the group to continue practicing. Emara leaves the practice, walking toward the garden in search of solitude under Loyola's tree. Finding it, she sits down and cries.

THE NEXT MEETING COMES QUICKLY. The volunteers include some of the group leaders, who surprise Calene by volunteering and providing replacements. Supplies are low enough that Calene says to cut food in half, causing grim faces around the table, but no one argues. The next days are spent preparing for the trip.

Emara and Suyana spend time each day before breakfast and before bed visiting with one another. They talk about many things, but the subject of the trip is never mentioned. The night before Emara's departure, Suyana sits next to Emara on the bed and holds her hand.

"How is the new outfit?"

"I think it will work nicely. Thank you for making it. I wonder how Father and my brothers are doing with the plans for the Joining. Do you think they will get it all done?"

"They will do their best, I am sure. Make sure you take your knife with you."

"I already have it on my belt."

An awkward silence resonates between them, then Suyana looks directly at Emara and grabs her hand. "Return safely, Emara."

Emara squeezes her mother's hand lovingly. "I'll do my very best." They sit in silence for a few moments, then the queen gets up, gives her daughter a hug, and kisses her on the crown of her head. She turns, blowing out the light, and goes to bed.

At dawn the group is ready to leave Arnac. Each person is heavily armed and protected with thickly padded clothing and helmets to protect the vital areas of their body. The plan is to get to the hunting ground, where the majority of people and horses will stay to hunt while a few continue on to Xenu. When the small group is done finding what happened at Xenu, they will rejoin the party at the hunting ground and work together to gather the other items on their way back to Arnac.

As the group starts, Emara looks back at her mother, waving a final goodbye. Taking a deep breath, Emara turns her mount, following the others through the gate toward Xenu and leaves the city behind. The scenery is beautiful outside the gates of Arnac as birds sing, bringing the forest alive with chatter. The party is alert to their surroundings and quiet, knowing that the robbers can be around any corner. Emara takes notice of places that look promising for obtaining the needed herbs as they quickly move forward.

Night descends rapidly in the forest, and the party does not light a fire, hoping to remain invisible to a possible attack, and eats only jerky, nuts, and dried fruit. Very few talk, keeping it to a minimum as they anticipate Gadianton. During the night the group takes turns standing guard duty, alternating every few hours so everyone has a turn to sleep before morning. But anxiety mixes with their dreams, awaking many as they rest with their swords in their hands. In the morning, they move forward, most of them walking. Everything is peaceful. They don't meet with a single robber by the time they arrive at the hunting ground.

The two women and two men who are to continue to Xenu help set up camp before traveling on. Emara is one of the women, and Loyola is the leader. As the distance to Xenu shrinks, their anxiety increases. They reach the top of a ridge to find a sea of red and black rushing toward them, trying to pull them from their horses. They withstand the raiders by using their swords. A robber that Emara is trying to deter manages to slice her outer thigh with his sword, pulling her off her mount. Emara falls to the ground with the robber on her, but she quickly maneuvers herself, grabbing her knife from her belt and stabbing before he can do the same to her. Adrenaline flows as she tries to push the dead man off her, recalling the last attack by Gadianton, but she is being trampled as the other robbers continue forward, trying to get away from whatever is coming. Her mind flashes back to Limhi's death. *How am I going to get out of this?* Something heavy steps hard on her foot and lower leg, making her scream with the pain. A panicked horse squeals loudly, standing on its hind legs in an effort to disperse the sea of robbers as they try to climb on its back. Something flashes before her vision, coming down toward her face. *That's my horse.* The horse's foreleg clips her head, knocking her out. Emara's mare gallops away.

AMMON

AMMON IS ONE OF THE MEN leading the attack against the robbers and is perched on his horse located on a hill nearby to watch the attack and give orders. He sees a small group on horseback come into view, trying to ward off the retreating robbers as they are separated from each other. His army is closer to three of the horses, while one needs help. Kicking his steed to bolt forward, he quickly works his way through the retreating robbers toward the single rider fighting for their life. He gets close enough to see a woman's shocked face as it disappears from view.

A mixture of emotions engulf him, but anger wins, moving him forward until he reaches the area where the woman has fallen. Ammon protects her with his steed and sword, warning all who are retreating to stay away while he wonders if it was his sister. He communicates to his men to continue to press forward in pursuit of the Gadianton robbers while he waits until his warriors have passed to dismount. What remains in the aftermath are the dead, the injured, and three very confused people.

Loyola sees Ammon and gets off her mare, tossing the reins to another, then running straight into his arms. "Where's Emara? I can't find her. Did you see her?"

He blinks away tears that come to his eyes as relief to see his sister is replaced with dread. He rips himself away from her and runs to the pile of bodies where he last saw the woman and starts moving bodies while Loyola follows. Loyola hollers to the others, "Get a healing pack." One person is quick to the task while the rest of the group help work through the bodies trying to find Emara. They move away a large body of a dead Gadianton warrior to expose Emara's unconscious, broken body covered in blood.

There is a head wound and a large wound on her upper outer thigh. He sees Emara's chest rise and fall. "She's alive."

"The body on top of her actually protected her." Loyola drops to her side with the healing pack.

Ammon carefully turns Emara into a more aligned position. "Emmy, I'm here. It's Ammon. You're alive, but hurt. Stay with me."

Ammon tears some cloth, making a compression dressing for the deep wound on her thigh while Loyola pulls out some herbs to make a poultice. Once the poultice is made, Ammon removes the cloth from the wound and Loyola applies the poultice directly to the wound, causing coagulation to start to occur. Then he reapplies the compression dressing and ties it in place. Loyola adds some herbs to the wound on Emara's head and then dresses it while Ammon continues to assess Emara. "Stay alive."

"Ammon, a lot of the wounds look superficial, which is good."

Ammon gets to her lower legs and feet, finding the fractures. "Find something to restrain her legs." The group starts looking for something sturdy that could be used to set the fractures.

"Are the bones displaced?"

"No." With the others' help, Ammon immobilizes Emara's leg and foot.

Once he finishes his assessment and care, he gets back up, blowing out the breath he unknowingly held. "Emara is alive but seriously hurt, which means we cannot move her."

"You can't stay here. There is no water, and the Gadianton robbers may find their way back."

"I know." Ammon slices his hand through his hair, walking toward the cliff. Looking out over the cliff, he scans the ravine below and sees a big tree at the bottom of the ravine near the river.

Loyola follows after him to the edge of the cliff. "What are you thinking?"

"You are correct, we can't stay here. What if we move Emara down the cliff using a sling? She could be nursed under the tree there, and the water is nearby. It will take a long time before she heals—one to three moons. I can make a canoe to travel to the hunting ground, and then we could walk back from there."

"Emara is in pretty bad shape, Ammon." Loyola rests a hand on his shoulder.

"I know, but I have to try."

Loyola nods her head. "It may work. We will come with you."

"You must continue. You need to tell my men that I am alive, but they must not come back for me. They must continue with the plan to stop the Gadianton robbers. After that, you need to get word to Emara's mother, since she will be worried about her."

"She will be worried sick knowing her daughter is hurt. Let me stay with her."

"As much as I trust you, I would worry too much about both of your safety, and you are not strong enough to tend to all her needs on your own. I don't trust anyone else because I don't know them." He puts a hand on his sister's shoulder. "Reassure her mother. Tell her that I'm taking care of her."

"You're not giving her much choice."

"Let me worry about that."

Ammon and Loyola walk back to the group, explaining the plan. They place Emara on a blanket, and the small group carries her to the edge of the cliff using the makeshift stretcher. Next, they carefully strap her to Ammon's back with the blanket around her to hold her in place. Finally, Ammon takes the rope and ties it around himself, getting ready to move to the ravine. The small group anchors the rope and helps control the rope while Ammon descends over the edge with his precious cargo.

At the bottom, he releases the rope and walks under the tree with Emara still on his back. His arms are shaking with the exertion of climbing down the cliff, and he has to wait a few minutes for the shaking to subside. Once the trembling is minimal, Ammon unties Emara from his back and gently lays her on the ground within the blanket, then walks back to the foot of the cliff.

"I'm dropping some supplies before we go," Loyola shouts to him. "You will need them."

After a little bit of time, several packs come over the ledge. Ammon retrieves them when they reach the bottom.

"Thank you, Loyola."

"You both stay alive! We'll be at Arnac."

Ammon returns to Emara, who is still unconscious. It worries him, but he is grateful that he has a plan in place.

He proceeds to find some stones to create a barrier from the elements and sets up camp. Once camp has been set up, he comes and sits by Emara. "It's time to wake up, Emmy."

The last thing Emara recalls is a horse coming down on her. Now she's in a fog. She hears someone calling to her. With hearing comes searing pain she does not like, so she instinctively moves away from the pain and drifts back to oblivion. She is pulled back every now and again by soothing words mixed with intense pain. She dreams of Mother on a family outing cooking fish that smells so good and realizes she's hungry.

Cooking fish nearby, Ammon hears Emara's stomach growl and frowns. Keeping Emara hydrated with fresh water has been a priority, but Ammon knows she needs food soon. He takes some of the fried fish and mixes it with water to make a broth for her to drink and seasons it with some herbs.

Emara realizes that her body hurts, and when she tries to move there comes excruciating pain.

"Easy there, Emmy. Lie still." Soft words come from Ammon. "Your horse stepped on you. I'm here."

Emara tries to open her eyes but can't. Her body is being moved slightly, which hurts.

"Drink this."

She feels something at her lips that smells so good, and she takes several gulps of the warm liquid before she registers the taste. Her face immediately wrinkles up, and her body shivers. She coughs and sputters, trying to remove the foul taste from her tongue. Feeling the cup that Ammon is holding toward her lips, she moves her face away, intending to avoid drinking anymore.

"Drink it all, Emmy. It will help with the pain."

Emmy calms down, weighing the choice before her. She finally turns her face toward the cup and drinks the awful-tasting stuff. It warms her belly, and soon she falls back to oblivion.

Emara dreams of being on the precipice on a warm summer day, and the stones at her back are warm. The sun is warm, mixing with a cool breeze. She hears a buzzing sound that turns into the sound of rushing waters. Her body aches, and the sound continues getting louder before being punctuated by a loud crack. She jumps, yet her body remains warm. The crack comes again. *What is going on? I must open my eyes.* Emara concentrates on doing just that. Her eyes open to see darkness before her, but she knows the sound. Lightning dances and thunder roars.

"Easy, Emmy," a soothing voice whispers in her ear while an arm comes around her to keep her still. "It's just a storm. You're safe."

Awake but too weak to move anymore, Emara tries speaking, but words don't come. Ammon turns her gently toward him as she grimaces but remains awake. The warmth at her back is now gone as Ammon's eyes come into view.

"Hello, Emmy." He smiles. "There's just a storm blowing."

Emara recognizes Ammon's voice and face. *What beautiful eyes.* Ammon watches Emara's face, seeing understanding and questions. She tries to speak again but the words won't come.

"Save your strength Emmy. You've been sleeping. It's good to see you awake."

The fog comes back, and her eyes close. This time she dreams of the evil man who sliced her leg and pulled her off her horse. Her dream moves to her mare crashing down on her. She feels a warm, comforting arm around her and settles.

She awakens to find that it's daylight, and her stomach

rumbles. She tries to sit up but falls back as dizziness, a severe headache, and nausea hit her.

"Easy Emmy. Let me help you." Ammon puts down the cup in his hand and sits behind Emara to help her to sit up against his chest. While he does this, a moan escapes her. "You will need to rest. Let me help you while your head and body recover." Once Emara's nausea passes, Ammon picks up the cup. "Drink."

Emara does what she is told, finding the same foul-tasting drink. Wrinkling her nose, she forces it down and realizes she is naked under a blanket. "Why?"

Ammon is puzzled by her croaked-out question but pleased she is able to speak. He looks down at her face, trying to decipher the question, and sees a rosy blush and eyes that won't look at him. "You're injured, and your bodily functions continue. I have to keep you clean and dry."

Emara takes this information, realizing that is what would be done in the infirmary, and relaxes against the hard chest, looking around and trying to take in the scenery. Ammon explains their location. He feels her body go limp against his chest, and her breathing becomes rhythmic. As gently as he can, he lays her down again to rest. While she sleeps, he gathers supplies for their extended stay.

Daily, Emara makes progress and is awake for longer periods of time. After a couple of days, her voice is strong enough that she is able to ask and answer questions.

"Why were you in the crowd at Uthal?"

"I came to see you. I come every year."

"Why?"

"I come to see you." Ammon states again as he sits behind her, combing her hair.

"That does not explain why."

Ammon chuckles. "No, it doesn't. Being a princess, has your mother not talked to you about a husband?"

"She has mentioned that one day I must choose one. I am not ready for that, so I choose the Challenge."

"I see." Ammon continues combing the knots out of her long, luxurious hair. "Is that why you train with your brothers? You've been training for many years."

"How do you know about that? We would practice where no one would see."

"You would practice early every morning with your brothers near the lake by the big rock. People could have seen you . . . my uncle would take me to Uthal once a year. When I was in Uthal, I liked watching you practice and made a point to be up early to watch from a distance."

"How did you find out about it?"

"I like to ride my horse early in the morning, and one day I saw you and your brothers and watched. From then on I didn't miss a day when I was there in the city."

"It started off as a way to get my brothers to spend time with me. I have since discovered that I want to make my own decisions and I don't want to be ordered. My parents understand that . . . so they have accepted . . . my decision to take the Challenge." She yawns, and Ammon remains quiet, allowing her to succumb to sleep. He finishes combing out the tangles and braids her hair, then gently lays her down again.

AMMON NOTICES THAT EMARA IS sitting watching him while her hands fiddle with her braid, so he walks over to her and sits by her side. "Would you like something to eat?"

Emara shakes her head slowly.

"Why do you fiddle with your braid?"

Her eyes drop. "I don't know."

"I won't bite you, Emara."

"I don't like talking about myself." The silence between them becomes uncomfortable.

"Would you like to play a game?"

Emara looks at him warily.

"It is a simple game I play with my sisters. Here is a rock. One person hides the rock in one of their hands, and the other person chooses which hand contains the rock. If the person choosing guesses correctly, then they can ask the other person a question. The person must answer the question truthfully no matter how uncomfortable it feels. If the person chooses the empty hand, then the other person shows where the rock was hidden and asks a question. The person answering must always answer truthfully. Do you want to play the game?"

Emara eyes him, and her hands absently play with her braid while he waits patiently for her response. She finally nods her head.

"Would you like to hide the rock or find the rock?"

"Hide."

Ammon nods his head, handing over the pebble. Emara places her hands behind her back and then brings them forward, closed tightly in fists.

Ammon looks at the fists before him and looks at Emara smiling. "Right."

Emara opens her right hand, showing it is empty, then opens her left hand to show the rock. "Why did you bring me here?"

"You were too injured to be moved and needed time to heal."

"Why did you not allow a woman to tend to me?"

"That is another question. Hide or choose?"

"Hide."

Placing her fists before him, she looks at him, determined to get more answers.

"Right."

She slowly opens her fist, showing the rock.

"My turn. Why do you fiddle with your hair? Don't tell me you don't know."

She sighs deeply. "When I think, my hands play with my braid. I can't stop it.

"Very good. See? It's not so hard. Would you like to hide or find?"

"Find." She passes over the stone.

Ammon takes the small stone and hides it behind his back, then displays both closed fists.

"Left."

Ammon reveals the stone in his left hand.

"Was it your intention to force me to be your wife? Because I won't be forced. Handing me your necklace that way doesn't mean I've accepted it. As you can see, it's not around my neck. When we get back to Arnac, I plan on returning it."

He looks at her directly as she stares back at him with all her emotions showing in her face. The tension between them is thick, and Ammon feels her anger. "No, it is not, nor was it my intention to force you to do anything. You were injured and would not survive traveling to a city."

"Why did you give me your necklace?"

Ammon shakes his head and places his fists before her.

She looks down briefly at the fists and back at him, her eyes full of fire. "Left."

Without moving his eyes from hers, Ammon opens his left hand, revealing the stone. "I gave you my necklace because I hope you will accept me as your husband."

"We don't know each other."

"Now we can."

"And you didn't plan this?"

"No. I didn't want my sister out here alone with you, and I didn't know the others. I couldn't think of another option that would result in you living."

She watches his face, and the fire in her eyes diminishes as she accepts his response. "One more question. Why do you insist upon calling me Emmy, when my name is Emara?

"Emmy is a term of endearment that was given to you by your brothers when you were a baby. I like the name. Do you have a problem with your brother's calling you Emmy?

"No."

"Then why should I not be permitted to use it as well?"

"Because I don't know you."

"And now you can. Listen, you look tired. We can discuss this as many times as you like, but first get some rest." He gets up and moves back to the fire.

THEY HAVE BEEN AT THIS place for about two weeks now, and several times a day they play the game, getting to know one another better.

One evening Ammon hands her some of the bad-tasting broth to drink. "There are enough herbs left for three more days, then we'll be out."

After taking a distasteful swallow of the medicine, Emara looks at him.

"I don't know where to find the herbs you need. If we follow the river, it will take us to the hunting grounds. There are lots of animals, so we'll have to wait until you can walk to travel safely."

Emara finishes her medicine and looks at Ammon again. "You are right that I can't walk, but we can't stay here. My mother must be worried sick. I believe I am well enough to travel now. I know where to get the herbs. Can we ride along the river?"

"I've been working on a canoe. It will not be comfortable, but it will get us down the river quicker."

"When will it be ready?"

"My guess is in a moon or two. We can only use it until we get to the hunting grounds, and then you will have to walk from there."

Emara looks at Ammon. "One or two moons? That long? So I take it we're staying here until I'm recovered?"

Ammon nods.

"What about the herbs?"

"Can you tell me what to look for and where to find it? I won't go unless you can keep yourself out of trouble."

Ammon watches as Emara's face changes from shock to embarrassment. When she looks up again at Ammon, her face exudes determination. "I think I can manage."

Ammon chuckles. "Just so you understand, I was teasing you."

"Oh, my brothers tease me. What can I do to help?"

"I'm sure I can think of something."

"What is the trade at Xenu?"

"We are a fairly small city. Xenu was a Nephite city around thirty years ago. My father inherited the city after his father reclaimed it. We have flint at Xenu. There are many things that can be done with flint. We also have an assortment of different colored stones there that are made into jewelry or taken to Uthal to be traded. We have traders who go to Uthal and bring things back that we need in the city. As I mentioned, my uncle is one of the traders."

They continue making plans regarding their persistent stay. She explains the herb she needs for the broth, since that is most important. "I also want to collect herbs that Arnac needs on our journey back."

That night they sleep well with the plan in place. In the

morning, Emara wakens to find breakfast made of eggs with wild onions and potatoes that Ammon found yesterday while he was looking for supplies within the area. After breakfast, the daily ritual of Ammon checking her injuries while changing her bandages takes place. "Your wounds are continuing to look good. You're making good progress."

After Emara is dressed, he carries her near the river, where he has the fallen tree, and deposits her on a smooth rock nearby. The fallen tree is being made into a canoe. He gives Emara long fibers to braid into rope. While they work, they continue talking with one another.

"I wonder how Loyola and the others are doing. I hope they made it back to Arnac safely."

"I have to think that they did." Ammon continues chopping chunks of wood from the fallen tree. "Loyola is smart, and my men will make sure that they make it back to Arnac safely."

"Your men?"

"Yes, my men. We were chasing after the Gadianton robbers when we came upon you trying to keep them away from your horses."

"What of Xenu? Are they all right? Are the people safe?"

"We lost many that were caught outside the city walls. The robbers tried many things to get into the city but were stopped."

"How did you get into Xenu with the city secured?"

"My family has a secret way into and out of the city, so I used it." He shrugs and continues slicing into the trunk. "None of the robbers saw me enter, and with the help of my father, we organized the city and planned our attack. The robbers had a limited amount of food with them, and we knew they would run out of supplies before we would. Therefore, we waited until their supplies were low, then attacked. It allowed us to gain the upper hand. You saw the aftermath."

"What was the objective?"

"To stop them from hurting anyone else."

Emmy nods. "Recently, we had an incident at Uthal. Father stated it was one of the least likeable kingly responsibilities he had to do. Peace was eventually restored, but at a cost. I don't recall how many died who opposed my father, but enough died that helped my father." After some time passes in silence, "How is your family?"

"They are all safe."

"Tell me about your family?"

"What would you like to know?"

"How many brothers and sisters do you have?"

"I have no brothers and three sisters."

"Are you the oldest?"

Ammon chuckles. "Loyola is older than me by about two years."

"What about your younger sisters?"

"Flora is three years younger than me. She'll see Arnac next year, and Palla is ten years old."

"How did Loyola learn to defend herself?"

"Father trained us both. It started when we were small when he would come and play with us in the garden every afternoon, which grew into training as we got older. She's very talented."

"Yes, she is. I like her a lot."

"That's good." Ammon looks at Emara before slicing another chunk out of the tree. "Believe it or not, Loyola was the first of us who was able to slay game for our table."

"Really? What was it?"

"A squirrel." Ammon takes another chunk out of the tree.

"What was your first catch?"

"A hive." Another chunk comes loose from the tree. "When I was about ten years old, Loyola and I went with our father on a hunting trip. It was good to be with Father because it was always an adventure. It was there she caught the squirrel. One day, I found a hive of bees and I thought it would be a great thing to take the hive home with us so that my mother and sisters could have honey all the time. I like honey as well." He grins at her and takes another bite out of the log. "Needless to say, I didn't know anything about gathering a beehive, and the closer I got to the hive, the more I got stung. The bees did not like me at all, but I continued to try. My father finally found me with my face and arms swollen with stings. I'm sure I looked a sight. He asked me what I was trying to do, but the evidence was all over me."

"Did you gather the beehive?"

"I was sick for two weeks after that and did not want to be around bees for a long time afterwards. But to answer your question, yes, Father showed me how to gather the beehive without getting hurt. We were able to bring the hive home, and Mother still uses it." Ammon continues telling stories about his childhood that make her laugh as he works on the canoe.

By lunchtime, the rope has been braided and Ammon is sweaty from the hard work of carving the canoe. Seeing Emara looking tired and hearing her stomach call for food, Ammon walks to the fish trap to see if he caught anything. Finding two, he puts the fish in a pouch. Bag in one hand, Ammon walks toward Emara with rivulets of sweat pouring off his muscular body.

Emara holds up her hands as he advances. "Oh, no you don't. Go wash in the river, and then you can carry me back to camp."

Ammon stops in his tracks as he grins and chuckles. "My mother and sisters have made similar statements in the past not to touch them when I'm sweaty." Dropping the fish next to her, he heads toward the river to wash.

Emara hollers after his receding body, "If that is the case, why torment me with your sweat?"

Ammon returns, no longer sweaty but still wet with the remaining water cascading off his body and clothes. He reaches Emara and scoops her up as she squeals. His skin is cool and strong. "So I can hear you squeal."

"You sound like my brothers."

Back at camp, he places Emara gently on the makeshift bed under the tree bough, and she hands the bag of fish to Ammon. Ammon takes the bag and goes to the fire to make the broth for Emara.

"I don't need the broth right now." Emara grins at him. "But I could use some food."

He nods. "You let me know when you need some more medicine."

"I will."

Ammon prepares the fish and cooks it over the fire, adding some herbs to season it while Emara watches. Once the fish is cooked, he puts it on a thin flat stone and brings it over to Emara. He sits next to her, and they share the fish in quiet companionship.

"Would you like some water?"

"Please."

Ammon hands the waterskin to Emara. She drinks and hands the waterskin back.

"You keep it," he says. "I'm leaving a knife and spear next to you so you can take a nap while I am at the canoe."

RECOVERY

EMARA WAKES UP TO FIND it is late in the afternoon and itches to be more productive. Knowing that Ammon is working on the canoe, Emara decides to use her arms and her knees to pull herself around camp rather than wait for Ammon. She attaches her belt around her clothes and sheaths her knife. She is careful with her broken bones, one on her left foot and the other on her right lower leg, which are bound by sticks. The sword wound is healing on her left upper leg, but she adds another layer of bandaging to help keep it clean. Pulling herself and the spear to the fire, she adds some branches to fuel the embers and pours water from the waterskin to fill the pot that Loyola left them. She adds some jerky to the pot and places it on the fire to heat up. After preparing the medicine in a cup, she gathers the remaining vegetables, chops them up on the stone, and puts them to the side. Once the jerky boils, she pours some of the boiling water into the cup, making the medicinal tea with the last of the pain medicine. Putting the cup to the side to cool, she adds the vegetables and some herbs for seasoning to the pot and stirs every so often. After drinking the cooled tea and stirring the pot, she drags herself around, managing to clean up much of the camp clutter. Back at the fire, she stirs the stew once again, realizing she is getting tired. She hopes Ammon will return soon. Hearing footsteps, Emara looks to where the sound is coming from.

Ammon walks around the tree to find what looks like a dirt-encrusted creature smiling happily with sticks poking out of her hair and stirring something in the pot by the fire. While the food smells delicious and the camp area has been organized, Emara looks a sight, stopping him short. After taking in Emara and his surroundings, he comes to the fire and squats next to her. "You have been busy."

"I have," Emara returns, smiling broadly. "I'm glad you're back."

"I think I found what I think is yarrow and birch bark." Ammon presents Emara with a whole yarrow plant with a bag around the roots and dirt. He also presents her with a bag containing the bark. She examines the plant he brought back using the waning daylight and the fire as a light. Her eyes light up, and she smiles at him. She quickly looks in the bag to find the bark she needs for the pain medicine, causing her to sigh in relief.

"You did well. Can you please plant the yarrow now before it is to dark? It needs to be in an area that has good drainage and full sun." She hands Ammon the yarrow, and Ammon takes it outside the camp and plants it while she watches from a distance. While Ammon plants the yarrow, Emara dishes out the stew on the stone to cool. When he returns, she hands him the stone, which Ammon promptly sets down, picking her up and moving her away from the fire before her clothing catches fire.

"Oh. I didn't realize . . ."

He sits down between the fire and her in the dirt now that she is safe and picks up the stew-filled stone, blowing on the food until it cools enough to pick up with hands. They eat quietly for a while, and once the stone is empty, Ammon dishes out another helping of stew.

"How's the canoe coming along?"

He removes the stew from the fire and returns to her side. "I didn't work on it this afternoon because I felt the herbs were more important. I can work on a paddle here at camp." He takes another bite of the stew. "The food is good."

Emara takes another bite of food. When her mouth is empty, she says, "Are we ready for tomorrow?"

"Almost." Once done eating their meal, he asks, "Don't you need some medicine?"

She shakes her head. "I had some before making dinner." He nods and covers the remaining stew with a cloth to be used for breakfast, then returns to Emara's side.

"Emmy, you've worked very hard today, and you will feel and sleep much better if you are clean." There is a pause as he looks at her. "You're covered in dirt."

"Oh, I suspected as much. I feel like I'm covered in dirt."

"Ready?" He grins at her.

"Now? It's nearly dark!"

"I'm not waiting until morning." Getting up, he scoops her into his arms and walks back to the river. He doesn't stop but walks right into an area that is not part of the main channel, but a side current that isn't as strong and is shallower. As the cold water hits Emara, she gasps, hanging on to Ammon as he continues deeper into the water. Once the water is deep enough, he looks at her face, getting her attention. "Your hair needs cleaned. Hold your breath."

"Oh no—"

Ammon bends his knees, taking both of them under the

water, and then straightens a moment later to return them above the surface. Emara sputters with the shock of the cold water. Without a word, Ammon turns and carries her back to the fallen log near camp, where he sets her. He picks up the blanket that he previously deposited there and shakes it out once, then holds the blanket up, creating a wall between them. "Try removing your clothing so I can wrap you in the blanket."

She is unable to do so by herself and looks up at him, "I can't. My shirt is clinging to my skin."

He lowers the blanket slightly and nods in understanding. "Hold the blanket with one hand to cover yourself. That's it. Lift one arm up." Emara looks down during this process, covering her front with the blanket. He reaches over the blanket, grabbing the wet shirt, then pulls it up over her arm until her arm is free. "Now the other side." He pulls the wet shirt and places on the bark. "I will hold the blanket while you untie your skirt."

Emara complies while the blanket creates a wall between them. "It's done." Ammon wraps her loosely in the blanket.

"I am taking off my shirt so I don't get this blanket any wetter than it already is. My goal is to get you dry, and we still have your skirt to remove."

Emara nods her head as she continues to look down.

Ammon pulls his shirt off and drops it on the bark near the other discarded shirt. "I'm going to pick you up now and find your skirt under the blanket and pull it off. Are you ready?"

Emara nods slightly, still looking at the ground.

"I can't see your face. Are you ready?"

"Yes."

Ammon picks her up around her blanket-covered waist. The fingers from his other hand skim upward along her leg, shooting little bolts of electricity up her leg while her stomach flip-flops. When he finds the wet fabric, he pulls gently until it releases its hold on her body. He drops the wet garment on the tree trunk with the other items and adjusts her in his arm before carrying her over to the bed, where he gently deposits her in a sitting position. By this time Emara's stomach is in knots with how he makes her feel.

Seeing Emara's discomfort and need to be alone for a minute, Ammon does not look at her, turning himself away to grab dry clothes for himself. He walks around the tree to the other side to change. After changing, he retrieves a branch from the fire, using it as a torch. He walks to where the wet clothes are piled and lays them out to dry overnight. He returns to their belongings and retrieves some items from a pack before positioning the torch nearby to give light. "I need to change your dressing. Is that all right?"

"Yes."

He nods and goes to work by firelight, dressing the wound on her thigh. Underneath her lashes, Emara watches him as the light dances upon his face. When the dressing is done, he gently changes the bindings around her broken limbs for dry ones, then looks up, catching her looking at him, which causes her to turn crimson. She drops her eyelids.

Because it is dark, he just sees a glimpse of an awkward look, but he continues to get up, concentrating on his task. "I'm going to sit behind you now and comb out your hair." Without saying another word, he positions himself behind her, working to take out her long braids, gently removing the remaining sticks and tangles from her wet hair using the comb like he has done many times before.

Over time Emara relaxes as he performs this simple task and she holds the blanket around her. He starts braiding her hair again finishing up the task when he hears, "Thank you. I think."

Ammon chuckles. "It was cold for me as well. You've now been restored to a human and not a dirt-encrusted animal, and you'll sleep better this way." Emara is quiet and tired as she debates with herself about leaning back against his chest now that she is getting better. Ammon clears his throat and moves to get up. "You're tired. It's time to sleep." Ammon settles Emara down for the night under a blanket and removes himself and the torch, taking it over to the fire. He watches her quickly fall asleep while he works on the paddle. After working for some time on the paddle, he looks up over at the sleeping form and smiles.

Early in the morning, Emara is startled awake by something. She finds Ammon's arm draped over her, and she can hear his rhythmic breathing. His hand is near the spear next to her, and her stomach somersaults. In order to shake the feelings she has, she tries to look around her but sees nothing. She squirms, trying to move the arm away, but the arm tightens around her like a snake coiled around its prey, which causes the butterflies in her stomach to intensify. Wanting to put space between them, she's ready to pinch him to get his attention.

At the same time, behind her, close to her ear, she hears, "Be still. I'm awake. There's a young brown bear eating our breakfast."

She immediately stills as butterflies disappear. She hopes the animal will eat quickly, then leave the area. They lie there together, listening intently for the bear as Ammon's arm loosens, returning to within easy reach of the spear. As dawn continues to reveal their surroundings, it's easier for Ammon to watch the animal. Finally, the bear finishes what's in the pot and walks toward the river. Ammon quietly gets up, grabbing bow and arrows, spear, atlatl, and his knife. He looks back at Emara, nodding to her as he disappears.

Sometime later, Emara sees Ammon return. After depositing some of his hunting gear, he brings her dried clothes and picks up the whetstone and pot, then disappears again toward the river. Emara uses the time he's gone to dress herself while her spear is within easy reach. When he returns, he picks her up and heads toward the river. "We have meat and need to dress the bear before another animal is drawn to it." He deposits her on the smooth rock near the river and gives her branches to ready for the meat that will soon come. Once everything is in place, Ammon talks to the young brown bear. "We thank you for giving your life. It was not given in vain. Your fur will keep us warm and your body will keep us full. Thank you for your sacrifice."

Ammon cleans the animal, handing Emara cut pieces of meat that she attaches to a sturdy branch to be seasoned and dried out in the sun.

"This will feed us for many days," Emara says. "Do you think there are other bears in the area?"

"This bear was old enough to be on his own, and I don't think there are others, but I will make sure that we are safe." He places the internal organs minus the intestines in the pot to be boiled for food and feeds the intestines to the river. Once the meat has been hung to dry, Ammon takes the skin and sets it on a frame to dry in the sun. Ammon carries the pot back to the fire, then returns for Emara and places her near the fire. Then he stirs the pot, waiting for their meal of innards to cook.

"We will need to water and check on the yarrow plant today," Emara says.

"What do I need to do with the yarrow so that I can dress your wound?"

"You will need to cut some stems off the yarrow plant and bring it to me to prepare."

"I can water the yarrow after we eat."

"The herb I need is juniper. With all this meat, we need juniper to use to smoke the meat and ward off other animals." She starts drawing something in the dirt. "It is found in direct sunlight, probably away from the river. I have seen it along the road, and I think there should be some not far away from our camp if you check along the cliff face. It has a reddish trunk and spiky leaves, and the tree may have blue berries and cones. It also has a fragrant smell."

After stirring the pot, Ammon comes and takes a look at the picture in the dirt and asks some questions to get a better understanding of what to look for. He returns to the pot and stirs it again, then walks to the yarrow bush and cuts off a few branches, giving them to Emara. Once relieved of the yarrow, he returns to the pot and stirs the contents again to see if the food is cooked.

Emara works on removing the leaves from the yarrow branch and stores them in a bag, throwing the bare branch to the wood pile for the fire. She holds out the bag. "Ammon, here are the yarrow leaves, can you please hang it up in the sun to dry? After breakfast you can take several leaves out making the poultice for my wound while the remainder continue to dry for future use."

Ammon stirs the pot again before hanging up the bag as directed and returning a short time later to again mix the contents of the pot. "It's almost ready."

"Who taught you to cook?"

"My mother. She said if her daughters can learn to hunt, then her son should know how to cook and clean."

Her eyes widen as she looks at him. "That is very unusual."

"Yes, it is, but I'm grateful for the knowledge, as it has helped me many times in my travels."

After their meal, Ammon takes a look at her thigh wound and dresses it with another poultice, then checks her legs and feet. He waters the yarrow, following Emara's instructions while she watches from camp. When Emara is satisfied with the yarrow and her needs are taken care of, he crouches next to her, winking. "Stay out of trouble. I'm going to look for the juniper."

Emara smiles at him, finally understanding the message. A few hours later he returns, dragging juniper branches into camp and taking them to where the meat is located. Emara watches as he builds a smoking fire under the poles containing the drying meat. The smoke removes the assortment of flies that have gathered in the area.

IN THE MORNING, AFTER LOOKING at Emara's healing wound, he starts removing the binding around her broken bones to gently massage her feet and lower legs while they talk. When he is done, he refastens the sticks around her foot and lower leg, then heads to the river to work on the canoe or to go on some type of errand for Emara. Sometimes Emara will join Ammon by the canoe, working on a rope, one of the found and collected herbs, or food preparation. Sometimes she stays at camp resting or working on some project she deems necessary to their well-being, making it a peaceful time for the both of them.

Emara continues to recover, and before long, more than a moon has passed. Emara is now able to put some weight on her legs, and Ammon gives her the spears to use as a support to help her move around camp. Each day, after the morning massage, Ammon helps her practice walking.

"It is frustrating that I can't get up and go like I did before this injury."

"You will get there. Remember your patients and how

you had to start small and help them work their way up to restoring their full health? It is no different for you."

"Yes, but I never expected to be the patient."

"This experience will give you greater empathy as you deal with them in the future. Now we will try again." Emara walks a few feet using the spears to assist her. "Easy there. You do not want to overdo it and create a delay in your healing." She turns and walks back. "That is good. Would you like to join me at the canoe or stay here?"

"I will stay here today."

Ammon nods his head and grins. "Stay out of trouble."

Emara grins back, nodding and watching him depart. She spends the rest of the afternoon tidying up camp while she prepares some herbs and meat for storage.

Another moon is approaching, and the canoe is almost done, but by this time Emara is walking again without assistance. One day Emara is sitting on the bank of the river chopping herbs that she found while he works on the canoe. It is hot, and by lunch time, Ammon is shirtless and sweaty as he walks over to her. "Ready for lunch?"

"Yes." Emara packs up the herbs, then looks up as he approaches. "You need to wash before we go back to camp."

"How about I carry you?" He reaches out for her.

Emara laughs and moves out of his way, "Not while you're sweaty." Ammon continues to pursue her while Emara dodges out of his way, laughing.

Ammon, grinning, decides to speed things up. "I think you need a sweaty hug."

"That's disgusting." After dodging him once again, she looks back, taunting him with her eyes while she laughs. They continue the game of cat and mouse until finally Ammon catches her in his arms, scooping her up and making her squeal. Both are laughing as he carries her to the bathing area and walks in, holding her. The cold water causes Emara to gasp as the water gets deeper. Ammon allows her legs to fall but continues to hold her pressed against his chest. He looks into her eyes—there is laughter in them and something else that holds him. Emara looks back at him as she struggles to breathe, seeing love and happiness in his eyes. He leans down and kisses her gently, and she kisses him back, enjoying the feel of him. The kiss deepens, mixed with something else—desire. His arms tighten around her back, molding her body against his. Her arms involuntarily tighten around his shoulders, and she feel the strong muscles under her fingers. A fire ignites in her core with a promise of something beautiful.

DECISION

Ammon breaks the kiss. Breathing deeply, he gently lets go of her. "We will leave tomorrow." He dunks himself under the water and climbs out of the river. Standing there, she feels like she was just slapped and then deserted.

He stops on the bank with his back to her, breathing hard for a minute, then slices a hand through his wet hair. When his breathing has settled, he turns and holds out his hand for her. "I'm sorry. I had no right." Emara takes a steadying breath and moves toward the shore. She takes the offered hand as he helps her back onto the river bank. When Emara's feet are solidly next to him, Ammon drops her hand as if he is burned and quickly walks away. He recovers his shirt and puts it on, then stomps back to camp with Emara following.

They eat lunch in silence as the tension between them builds. After Ammon finishes eating, he stands up and stomps around camp, moving their belongings into the same area. "Can you pack up camp? I will get some supplies and return."

"Why are you like this?"

"Why am I like what?"

"You're distant. You're upset, and I can only assume it's toward me based upon how you're acting."

Ammon stops moving. Slicing his hand through his hair again, he takes a deep breath and turns toward her. "We kissed."

"Yes, and I liked it." Emara smiles.

"It can't happen again."

"Why?"

His eyes widen as he stares at her. "We're not joined!"

She blushes.

"Are you still planning on taking the Challenge?"

"Yes."

His mouth drops open. "Why?"

"Because I'm not ready to be joined to a man."

"We've been out here together for almost two moons, day in and day out, and you've gotten to know me."

Emara looks at him for a moment and shakes her head. "I'm not going to join you just because we've been out here together."

"Of course not. I have feelings for you, Emara." He takes some steps toward her. "I love you and I want us to be joined."

Emara takes some steps toward him, closing the distance. "I have feelings for you, but I'm not ready. Why can't we continue as we are?"

Ammon takes her hands. "We've got to go back. We have people who miss us, and when we get back it will be expected that you'll join me."

Shaking her head again, she pulls her hands away from him and steps away. "It may be expected, but I will not join you just because it is expected."

He glares at her. "Your parents may have other ideas."

Standing firm, she juts her chin out as she raises her head

a little higher, glaring at him. "My parents may have other ideas, but I will *not* be forced to join anyone. My parents could not force my brother, Helam, to join someone he has never met before. His arranged Joining was cancelled."

Ammon takes a step forward frowning. "That arranged Joining was to Loyola."

Emara's mouth drops open. "Loyola?"

"Yes." Ammon's face softens.

"Did you know that she is happy it did not occur?"

He takes a step forward. "No, what did she say?"

"She would rather be joined to someone she could choose, and so do I."

Ammon stands there staring at her for a moment as he fights with his feelings. "We are arranged to be joined. What's wrong with me?"

Emara's head reels back as her eyes widen and her mouth drops open again. "We are not! No one has said anything to me."

Closing his eyes, he takes a deep breath. "I wanted you to have the ability to choose for yourself, so they promised not to tell you. So what's wrong with me?"

"I didn't say anything was wrong with you. What I said was I'm not ready!" Emara glares at him.

Ammon runs his hand through his hair again, looking at no one in particular. "What does that mean?"

"It means exactly that. I'm *not* ready!" She stomps her foot with each word for emphasis. "You're not exactly letting me have time to choose for myself either." She frowns at him.

Ammon slices his hand through his hair a third time and takes another deep breath. He stomps around, grabbing a few supplies and stuffing them into a pack. "Stay out of trouble. I'll be back later." He stomps out of camp, not looking back.

Throughout the afternoon, she replays in her head what

occurred earlier that morning. It was wonderful, and now Ammon has distanced himself from her. She packs up camp, recalling often the kiss and the conversation that followed.

When Ammon returns late in the day, he presents Emara with a bag full of something. She opens the bag, finding it full of prickly pear.

"It's my favorite fruit." She looks up at him. "Thank you." Taking a breath, she lowers the bag and looks up at him again. "Ammon, I like being with you, and I want our friendship to continue even when this is over."

Ammon nods, then turns to taking the packed supplies to the canoe. Emara is left by herself again and she sighs.

Ammon returns to camp after dark, and she has dinner prepared for him—a stone full of stew. She ate hours ago and watches silently as he eats.

When he's done eating he looks up. "Thank you for dinner."

"I'm not going to get any sleep tonight until I know that we're all right."

Ammon takes a breath and looks at her. "We're friends, Emara. All is well. It's time that we sleep separately since your health is restored. Your life is yours." Ammon gives a halfhearted smile. "It's late. We'll have to start taking guard duty as we go forward to keep us safe. I'll take the first shift while you get some sleep." Ammon turns to tend to the pot of stew. Emara sighs and goes to bed as tears fall silently from her eyes.

ALÎVE

EMARA IS GENTLY SHAKEN, WHICH wakes her up. Ammon smiles at her kindly as she blinks away the sleep from her eyes. "Time for guard duty."

She nods and gets up while he takes her place and covers himself with a blanket. She walks over to the fire to keep herself warm and finds a clean pot and a full waterskin. She takes a drink of the cold water, which wakes her up even more and makes her shiver. She looks at the stars, realizing that Ammon let her sleep longer than he should have.

Watching the stars, she thinks about what her future would be like with him. She would have to move to Xenu, whereas her family would remain at Uthal. *Would I ever see them again? Could I live with that? Life without Ammon would be even worse.* She watches as the stars fade in the sky to reveal a beautiful dawn. She pours water in the pot and places it on the fire to boil. They saved the last of the cornmeal for their last morning here, and she pours it into the pot for their hot breakfast. Before long it is prepared. Emara removes the pot from the fire, then goes and wakes Ammon up. He grumbles, wiping the sleep out of his eyes while Emara smiles to herself and walks back to the fire.

A little while later Ammon walks over to the fire, finding that Emara has made breakfast. She scoops out the mush onto the stone and sits down, waiting for him to join her. He presents her with a carved spoon and keeps one for himself. Emara smiles at the present, taking the offered spoon, and they eat silently together. He refills the stone plate with the remaining mush and returns to her side, where she eats until she is full. Then he finishes the rest. Without a word he passes his wooden spoon to her and moves to clean out the pot with water from the waterskin. He tosses the dirty water on the fire.

"Good morning."

"Good morning."

Ammon finishes dousing the fire. "It's time to leave." Emara nods and stands up. After taking the two spoons in her hand, she cleans them off and stores them away in a bag at her waist, then picks up the two spears and hands one to Ammon. They both take a final look around before he picks up the last of their gear and carries it to the canoe, which is on the bank by the river tied to a tree. They tie remaining gear to the canoe, then Ammon lines up the thin branches he previously collected to help move the new canoe to the water and pushes. The canoe moves to the water with ease.

"Get in." Ammon holds the canoe so Emara can get in the front. After Emara is situated, he positions himself in the back and grabs the paddle. "We are ready. Untie the rope." Once the rope is untied, they move down the river with the current. On occasion, Emara tells Ammon to stop the canoe so she can gather some herbs, and he complies with her wishes. Later in the day, Ammon slows the canoe and points it toward the shore.

"Why are we stopping?"

"We're at the hunting ground, which means the rest of the way will be by foot. We'll have to move quickly and quietly, and we'll have to stay together at all times. Understand?"

Emara, wide-eyed, nods.

"Ready?"

Emara quickly gets out of the canoe and ties it up. Ammon gets out of the canoe and holds it in place while Emara unloads their supplies. Once the supplies have been unloaded, Ammon, with Emara's help, moves the canoe to the shore and turns it over. They load their supplies on their backs, and Emara follows Ammon through the forest. She hears birds of different species and lots of other sounds she has never heard before. She follows Ammon, trying to keep up with his fast pace. With the load on her back, she's panting before long. Ammon, hearing her labored breathing, stops and gives her the waterskin. She drinks some water and returns it to him, and he also drinks. He waits until her breathing calms down before starting again.

He starts the ascent again, this time at a slower pace that allows them to get farther before Emara is panting again. Ammon stops, allowing Emara to recover before moving forward. This pattern continues until dusk. He whispers in her ear, "It looks like it's going to rain tonight. We need to find shelter." She nods and continues to follow him along the cliff face. He points to a small, narrow cave to protect them from the elements and other animals. "We can camp here."

While Ammon lights a fire, Emara, takes out the pot and adds some water, herbs, and jerky to make their dinner. She is hungry, and her stomach growls like one of the animals she hears in the distance. She takes out a prickly pear and cuts it in half, handing one half to Ammon. Sitting next to the pot that is heating on the fire, she eats her half of the prickly pear.

Ammon looks for branches nearby to feed the fire during the night to ward off the animals. Emara sets up the cave with the bear fur and their belongings while the food cooks. Once the stew is ready, she removes it from the fire and hands Ammon his spoon, and they again eat silently.

"Sleep, Emara. I'll take first watch."

SHE AWAKENS. AS SHE MOVES over to the mouth of the cave where Ammon sits with his back to her, she finds it is raining. She touches his shoulder, and he glances at her. "When did the rainfall start?"

"A while ago, and it will probably continue until morning. It'll be slippery tomorrow. How are your legs and feet holding up?"

"They are good. I'll take over while you get some sleep." He nods his head and briefly squeezes her wrist in a thankful motion before moving deeper into the shallow cave, where he quickly falls asleep. Emara sits watching the rain with the spear next to her as her eyes adjust to the dark. She notices the pot outside the mouth of the cave is now full of water and decides to drink from the waterskin.

The rain finally stops, and insects come out making the forest come alive with the sounds of small animals searching for food. Emara watches, intently aware of her surroundings. She sees as an owl swoop down to retrieve its prey just before daylight dawns in the forest. A warm hand connects with her shoulder, causing her to jump.

"I feel it too," Ammon says. "Leave the pot. It'll slow us down. We can eat other things." Moving outside the cave, Ammon stretches, motioning to Emara to keep guard. He quickly gets ready for the day and refills the waterskin with the water in the pot. He quickly packs up the gear and places his on his back, then passes Emara the remaining backpack, indicating it is now her turn while he stands guard. Ammon looks to her, and she nods, indicating she is ready to move. He points to where they are headed up the ridge, indicating she is to go first. Behind them, a mountain lion starts tracking them.

Emara starts up the slippery slope one foot at a time, endeavoring to find good footing with each step while trying to move quickly. The steeper the climb, the slower their progress. Several times she slides backward and Ammon stops her descent and pushes her forward again. Several times it is slick enough that both Emara and Ammon slide backwards, then start forward again as she continues to push her way up the slope.

"Emmy, left." She looks left to see a mountain lion working its way up the slope while its eyes focus on Emara and Ammon. "We're being hunted."

She picks up her pace, but with the heavy pack and the recent rainfall, it's hard to climb up the slope. Emara is tired but knows she cannot stop and must reach the top. Ammon continues to push her forward as she struggles up the incline. Looking left again to see where the mountain lion is, she finds it's gone. She looks up the slope to see if she can find it.

Finally, she sees the mountain lion coming down the slope, charging toward them. Just then her footing fails, and she falls. Ammon, spear ready, moves his weapon forward just moments after the mountain lion jumps. The big cat lands on Ammon, and the weight and force of it knock Ammon down the steep hill with the mountain lion. Emara screams, dropping her pack and going after Ammon. She flies down the hill, her adrenaline pumping and spear ready to attack the mountain lion or any other creature that crosses her. She arrives at the bottom to find the big cat lying still.

"Where are you, Ammon?" The mountain lion moves,

and she spears the animal. Afterward, she realizes the mountain lion is dead with the end of a spear sticking out of its neck, and something under the cat is struggling to free itself. Emara pushes the carcass to the side, revealing a bloody Ammon. Emara drops to her knees, looking all over Ammon's head and chest to find the source of the injury.

"I am fine, Emmy."

Emara doesn't hear him speak, so keen is she on finding the injury and taking care of it.

Ammon works his way out of his pack with Emara still looking for wounds. He grabs her arms and holds them, looking into her eyes. "I'm fine. The blood is the mountain cat's. Let's go." She's pale but nods in understanding. Standing up, she grabs her spear while he gathers his spear and backpack. Adrenaline fills them both as they proceed back up the hill, grabbing her pack on the way, until they reach the top.

At the top of ridge, she finds the meadow where they left the hunting party, but it's empty. Emara feels like her lungs are on fire and struggles to breathe. She looks at Ammon, whose head and chest are covered in blood, struggling to breathe as well as he pushes her forward to continue farther into the meadow. Finally, Emara can go no farther and falls to the ground, where he joins her, gasping for air. After regaining some air, Emara and Ammon remove their packs and sit, spears in hand, trying to recover from the climb.

"You look . . . a sight."

"At least . . . we are . . . alive." Ammon grins at her. "You're . . . covered . . . in dirt again."

"Better than . . . blood." She grins back. "What . . . now?"

After a time, Ammon takes out the waterskin and drinks some water, then hands it her way. She takes it gratefully and drinks. Ammon waits until his breathing is under control. "We continue on." Emara nods. They put their packs back on

and proceed on the muddy track leading back to Arnac. The
trail still leads up, but at a smaller incline than before. They
walk silently next to each other. Emara finally stops, not able
to go any farther, and looks at Ammon, panting. He under-
stands and nods, turning to search for a place to make camp.
He returns a short time later without his gear and takes
Emara's pack from her, leading the way to a small cave where
he lays down the bearskin and pulls out the blankets. Climbing inside the cave after Emara and closing the mouth with
the packs, he covers himself and Emara with the blanket,
and they quickly fall asleep.

TRAVEL

EMARA'S STOMACH GROWLS FIERCELY, AWAKING both occupants of the cave.

Ammon chuckles. "It seems it is time to eat."

"It is. I'm hungry."

Ammon moves to the packs and takes out two prickly pears as well as the jerky bag. "Let's eat outside where there's more room." He moves slowly due to sore muscles from their exertion earlier but finds a nice breeze outside the cave. A full moon in the sky shines brightly, lighting the night, and the stars twinkle in the distance. Emara slowly works her way out of the cave as her muscles scream in protest. When she stands up outside the cave, a moan escapes her lips. Ammon then rewards her efforts with a piece of fruit that she carefully holds as she removes the skin. She digs in, happily eating while a drip of juice slides down the side of her mouth. Once done with the fruit, she takes a piece of jerky.

"If you have daughters one day, will you teach them to defend themselves?" she asks.

Ammon looks at her for a moment and finishes the fruit in his mouth. "I don't see why I wouldn't teach them." He takes another bite of the fruit he has in his hand, relishing the taste.

Emara looks at Ammon in the moonlight with all the dried blood and dirt over him. "If you look bad, I probably look worse. I'm looking forward to getting clean when we reach the city."

Ammon looks at Emara, finishing what is in his mouth. "One more day, possibly two, before we reach Arnac. "How are your feet and legs?"

"Right now, everything is sore."

"Me too. Let me take a look at your foot and leg just to make sure." Emara finds a place to sit, and Ammon sits next to her, evaluating her foot and leg. He massages each appendage, and she moans in delight as he works out the soreness.

"Your bones feel good. Better?"

"Yes."

"Think you can make it?"

"I may be slow starting." She moves her arms, wincing at the soreness. "My muscles are really sore."

"So are mine, but we'll do it together." Emara looks at him and smiles. "How do you feel about being away from your mother?"

"I miss her." Emara takes another bite of the jerky.

"Are you all right being away from her?"

"You've made it bearable." She looks at Ammon with gratitude in her eyes. "Thank you for taking care of me."

Ammon nods, acknowledging her statement. They continue to eat pieces of jerky until they feel better. With very little water left in the waterskin, they choose to save it for tomorrow. Emara and Ammon both have sticky hands from the fruit. While cleaning her fingers with a leaf, Emara looks at the scenery around her. "What a beautiful night. It reminds me of my favorite place to sit and think. The only difference is that there is a lot of vegetation here. There . . . it's just rock."

"What makes it so special?"

"It's high in the rocks, and I can see the whole valley up there. I can think there without interruption."

"What do you think about?"

"Lately it has been about taking the Challenge. I made the decision to go."

"And now?"

"This has really been tough physically." She looks at Ammon, "I'm not sure if I want to go on the Challenge if it is anything like this. I will have to think about it."

"You can choose a husband."

"I can . . . but I won't. I'm not ready for that."

Ammon nods. "We need to get some sleep to start again in the morning. I will take guard duty."

"Do we need it now?"

"It would be good for both of us."

Emara frowns. "Just so you know, I don't like it, but I understand the need." She turns, goes into the cave, covers herself with the blanket, and tries to sleep. She has a nice dream about Ammon joining her on her precipice. He likes it, and they sit there holding hands. Something shakes her foot, waking her up from the dream. She looks to find Ammon.

"It's time."

Emara crawls out of the cave with her stiff, sore muscles, and Ammon climbs in, placing the blanket around her shoulders before lying on the fur to sleep. The moon has moved across the horizon when she sits at the mouth of the cave with her spear in hand. She thinks about the dream and how it felt and smiles. "I love that man."

Her mother's words echo from the past: *Just because you love a man does not mean he is fit to have as a husband.* Her hand absently reaches for her braid. It was a long time ago when those words were said to another. Emara was working in the infirmary when a woman was brought in. She'd been beaten by her spouse. She looked horrible and spent several weeks in the infirmary. Emara couldn't understand why her husband beat her, so she asked her mother. She explained that not all spouses are kind or a good partner. After that experience, Emara listened and watched other parents, how they worked together and how they treated their children. Mother stated once that Joining is a state of mutual service to one another. Emara found that some women didn't like their husbands, and she found that there were some men who expressed that they didn't like their wives. She also found that there were couples who were unkind to one another. Her mother's words again reverberate through her. *It is a poor environment for children.* Uthal law stipulates that once a spouse is chosen, it is for life. The law also states that if you kill your spouse, your life is forfeit. She recalls her father words, *These are sad times for those who have to uphold the law.*

Emara observed that parents also had a say in how well or how poorly the joined treated their spouses. If a parent didn't care for their child's partner and treated them unkindly, chances were the child would follow their parent's example and treat their spouse the same.

Emara watched her parents closely over the years, noticing that they continue to be kind to one another and serve each other. They even still work well together. She recalls many other examples of good partnerships that she has observed, and she smiles to herself again. *I want the kind of relationship that my parents have. Can I have that with Ammon?* Emara knows nothing of Xenu, and the only knowledge of his family is what was revealed to her. *Will his parents accept me? What will I do there? Will I be happy there?* So many questions flood her mind. "It would be so much easier to make a decision if he lived at Uthal," she mutters, noticing that Ammon stirs. She sits still, listening for Ammon's rhythmic breathing to resume. When she feels that Ammon has settled, she quietly moves farther outside the cave, trying not to further disturb him.

When she gets far enough away, she finds a place to sit with her spear in easy reach. "I must work through my questions." Her hands absently retrieve her braid and start fiddling with it again. "The first question is, does Ammon make me happy? That is an easy yes. Do we work well together? Another easy yes."

As she continues down her list of questions, they become harder to answer because she doesn't have all the information. "Loyola may be able to help me." She smiles to herself, thinking of Loyola and looking forward to seeing her friend again. The night sky fades while she is in deep thought, and the sunrise filters through the trees, pulling her out of her thoughts. "Soon it will be time to walk again." She sighs, standing up and stretching to work out her sore muscles. She realizes she is thirsty and hungry, causing her to pull out the jerky bag and take a bite from one of the pieces. She puts off her thirst, wanting to save the last of the water for later in the day.

Crawling on all fours, Ammon emerges from the cave with scrunched brows and a thin mouth. He stands up and stretches, working his soreness away. Emara watches him under her lashes as she chews on the jerky, trying to keep a straight face as he walks around. Emara finishes her piece of jerky, then goes and packs their supplies in the cave, giving him some privacy to start his day. When she backs out of the cave and stands up, she sees Ammon smiling at her. "Good morning."

"Hello. Did you sleep well?"

"Well enough. There is not much water left, and only two prickly pears. Do you want it now or later?"

"Later. We might need it later." Holding up the bag of jerky, she says, "There is plenty of meat left."

He takes the offered jerky bag and takes a piece out, then attaches the bag to his pack. "I agree with you." Ammon sees that her pack is twisted and helps straighten it. She nods an "I'm ready" to Ammon, and they both start off.

On the way, Emara finds some herbs and stops to collect them. Ammon helps her, following her instructions. Ammon asks her questions about the herbs she gathers. "What does the herb do?" "How must it be prepared?" Emara happily shares her knowledge of the herbs she collects, and Ammon enjoys the information that she gives.

Before long they are sweaty again, and Emara is sure she must already stink. She could smell Ammon's strong scent even after the first day, but after two days of traveling, it still does not repel her even though it's quite noticeable and flies have started to accompany them on their journey. They try to ignore the pesky companions but brush them away as needed. By midafternoon, Emara's throat feels like it has closed in on itself. Her mouth is dry and tacky, but she continues forward without conversation. Ammon stops her, handing over the waterskin, and croaks, "Drink." It's not a question, but an order.

Emara quickly grabs it, fumbles with the top, and finally drinks. The warm water feels delightful in her mouth and on her throat as she swallows. She would like to drink all the water but makes an effort to stop herself so Ammon's thirst can also be reduced, and she hands the waterskin his way. He looks at Emara, who nods, answering his unspoken question. He gulps the last of the water down, relishing the feeling. Breathing afterwards, Ammon replaces the cap and returns the waterskin to his belt. He moves his head slightly to the side, indicating they need to continue forward, and Emara falls into step beside him.

Emara no longer looks for herbs but now looks for signs of water throughout the afternoon until the sun begins to fade. Ammon finds a place to camp, this time along the road, where they rest in silence as they deal with their thirst. Ammon pulls out the prickly pear, silently offering Emara her pick, but she shakes her head and he returns them to the bag for later. Emara lies on the fur, exhausted, and quickly falls asleep while Ammon keeps guard sitting next to her. Her dreams consist of distant water she can't seem to reach and something stuffed in her mouth.

A hand rests on her shoulder, waking her from a fitful sleep as she struggles to sit up—she is dizzy. She is very tired but keeps her dizziness to herself as she takes her turn guarding. Ammon falls quickly to sleep and wakes before dawn, then pulls out the prickly pears and passes one to her. She uses her knife to cut the fruit, making sure that no juice drops to the ground and sucking the last of the fruit from its shell. After their meal, they get up, not bothering to wipe the remains from their fingers, and put on their gear. Ammon helps her as she struggles with her pack, then they walk toward Arnac again as dawn announces itself in the distance.

A little while later a sheet of rain descends, and both joyfully stand in the rain, opening their mouths to drink the rainwater as it falls. After relieving some of their thirst, they open the waterskin, intending to catch some water, but it doesn't work well. Emara looks around and finds a large leaf on a plant nearby. She quickly cuts the leaf and brings it to

Ammon to place above the waterskin to gather the water and guide it into the bladder. While Emara holds the leaf and Ammon holds the waterskin, they continue to open their mouths skyward, swallowing whatever rainwater they obtain while their eyes bounce back and forth between the leaf and the mouth of the waterskin, making sure the skin is filling with water. When the waterskin fills up, they each take turns drinking from the pouch. Each time the water in it is emptied, they fill it up again. The rain lasts for a while, leaving them soaked but smiling as Ammon returns the waterskin to his belt.

"I can see your face again." She smiles at him. "It's a nice face."

He looks up surprised by her comment.

Just then they hear a crashing sound descending rapidly down the side of the mountain next to them. They look to where the noise is coming from to barely see a mudslide coming their way. Ammon reaches out, grabbing the nearest deeply rooted item he can find with one hand and snatching Emara's arm with the other. The mud hits, knocking them over. Emara's wrist feels like it has a vice grip around it, and her arm feels like it's on fire as the force of the mud presses down on her, trying to drag her away from Ammon. As the mud gets deeper, she struggles to hold her breath as the weight of mud presses upon her chest. Flashbacks of being trampled come to her mind, and panic rises in her throat.

REUNION

Ammon is the first to emerge from the mud, and he turns to quickly dig Emara out. He pulls most of her body to the top and makes sure she is not injured. Her face that was clean moments before now has two eyes and two nose holes peeking out of mud. Ammon looks about the same, with his now loose hair poking out in one direction on the side of his head. They sit there on top of the mud, breathing hard looking at each other. Emara starts to giggle, and Ammon starts laughing. Before long they lie on their backs, both laughing hysterically.

"You should see your face," Ammon says.

"You should see yours. Your hair is full of mud poking out on the side of your head in one direction. So much for a clean face." They laugh again.

Ammon gets up, comes to her side, and helps her sit up again. "Close your eyes so I can clean most of the mud off your face. Right now, you look like a mud monster." Emara closes her eyes as Ammon gently removes the majority of the mud from her face.

"My turn."

Ammon closes his eyes and allows Emara to clear the muck from his face and hair.

"All done."

Ammon opens his eyes and looks at Emara as she stares back, unable to take her eyes from him. Her stomach flips, wanting him to kiss her again, recalling how good it felt the first time.

"We need to continue." Ammon squeezes her hand, breaking the moment. "I think we have a few hours left before we reach Arnac." Emara nods, trying to get free of the mud. Ammon digs her feet out and helps her across the mud. He returns to the mud and digs out her pack, shaking it, trying to help gravity remove the mud. He looks at something in his hand, then looks in the pack, closing it again. He climbs over the mud and hands the pack to Emara, smiling at her. "The contents are still clean." Back on the path, Ammon takes her muddy hand as they continue happily walking the trail. It's another sticky day. As time continues, the mud dries to the packs, their clothes, and anywhere on them that is not wet with perspiration. Rivulets of mud drip off their faces. They stop a few hours later and take a drink of water from the waterskin, then press on.

Turning a corner in the road, the duo come face-to-face with two guards with swords raised coming toward them. The strangers aren't dressed like Gadianton robbers, but they are unfamiliar to the both of them. Ammon steps in front of Emara, moving her farther away from the attackers. He blocks the first attacker as he slices through the air with his sword, then responds by injuring the attacker's forearm with his sword. The first guard drops his sword to the ground only to find that he now has Emara's spear at his throat. She kicks his sword out of his reach while Ammon turns to deal with the second attacker.

Emara concentrates on the first attacker yelling, "Who is your commander?" The first attacker is too interested in the swordfight going on near him to acknowledge her words, so she slightly pushes her spear farther into the attacker's throat, getting his attention. "Who is your commander?" she repeats.

"Enon."

Emara nods. "Enon is my brother. I am Princess Emara." The attacker looks at her for a little while, and then recognition lights his face. "Leave your sword alone, and I will dress your wound.

"Agreed." Emara removes the spear from his throat.

Just then the ping of swordplay stops. Both Emara and the first attacker look to see what happened. Ammon and the second attacker have disappeared, causing Emara to drop her spear and run to the edge of the cliff. Looking over, she sees the river far below, but no men. Emara yells for Ammon, but there is no answer. She yells again and again—there is still no answer. Emara's knees buckle as loss overcomes her, and she falls to the ground. The soldier comes and looks over the edge, calling for his companion, and receives the same answer as Emara. He looks at her sitting on the ground. Emara's eyes register the blood dripping from the soldier's arm wound and takes a breath. Removing the pack, she rummages for the healing pack. Not finding it, she finds a cloth that is not as clean as she would like but is better than nothing. She pulls out the appropriate herbs and dresses the wound with the herb covered by the cloth.

"What is your name?"

"Pagog."

"How far away is Arnac?"

"It's near here." The noise brought other soldiers. Seeing Emara dressing the soldier's wound, they recognize her as a friend.

"Two soldiers fell over the ledge," Emara says. "See if you can find them and return them to Arnac."

The soldiers look to the injured soldier, not recognizing the mud-encrusted woman. Pagog nods his head, and immediately the group goes to the edge in search of the missing men.

Once finished with the dressing, she looks at Pagog. "Take me to Enon." The soldier nods as she puts on the pack, struggling to stand. Pagog helps her up and leads the way back to Arnac. As Emara walks, she sees more Uthal soldiers.

"Did Enon bring an army to rescue Arnac?"

"We heard about the robbers, and Enon was assigned to bring us to help."

Before she reaches the city, word has spread to Enon and Loyola. When they see her, they both run her direction. Loyola reaches her first, engulfing her in a hug even though she is dirty and smelly. "Where is Ammon?"

"He fell over the cliff with another man. The other soldiers are trying to find them."

Loyola lets go of her and hands her off to Enon's care. She smiles quickly, "I'm glad you're back." She leaves to help with the search.

Enon hugs his sister. "I am glad you are back, Emmy. We—"

Emara's strength gives out, and she falls unconscious in Enon's arms. Enon quickly removes the pack, barking orders to another soldier to grab the pack and follow him. He picks up his sister, who feels lighter to him, and carries her into the city. As news spreads, Suyana shows up in the courtyard and sees Enon carrying a mud-encrusted person. She changes directions, running his way. When the queen reaches Enon, he doesn't stop, but continues to the infirmary as he explains to his mother what happened. Within the infirmary he deposits Emara on a bed and stands back, letting the queen evaluate her daughter. Enon's patience wears thin—his mother doesn't talk but continues to assess Emara. She asks Enon to help turn his sister so she can get a better look.

Once Suyana is done with her head-to-toe assessment, she turns to Enon. "Emara will be all right but must remain in the infirmary until she recovers. "Now scoot so I can attend her better." Enon pauses, not wanting to leave, but Suyana puts a hand on his arm, saying softly but firmly, "She is going to be all right."

Enon nods and heads toward the door, intent on helping Loyola in the search. On the way out of the infirmary, the guard who is holding the pack asks, "What about this?"

"Leave it here."

While the queen was assessing Emara, Pagog is taken by another to the other side of the infirmary to be treated. When the men are out of the way, the women work on caring for Emara. They bathe her and put her in a clean bed with a clean nightdress. Her legs are elevated with blankets under a sheet to get more blood back to her heart. With Emara's swallow reflex still intact, Suyana gives her a very small amount of broth to start the process of rehydrating her. After the first dose of broth, Suyana releases the breath she unconsciously held, knowing that Emara is alive and under her care.

The queen looks at the stinky, dirty pack lying on the floor and takes a deep breath as she gets to work. Opening the pack, Suyana finds an assortment of herbs that her daughter has gathered, which she takes out carefully and examines. "They are still good." Taking one of the herbs and putting it to the side, she calls over another person to take the remaining herbs for processing. Looking in the backpack again, she finds a dirty, well-used blanket, and the last thing she finds in the pack is a bluish-green colored-turquoise stone. She smiles, depositing the stone in her pocket to give to her daughter later. After the pack is emptied, the blanket and pack are handed to a woman to be taken outside and thoroughly cleaned for future use. The queen returns to her daughter's side, continuing to nurse Emara back to health by giving her the broth in intervals.

Outside the infirmary, Enon decides to wait for Pagog. When Pagog walks out of the door of the infirmary, Enon pulls him aside to get a report. "We saw two people walking down the road covered in dirt. We thought they were robbers and attacked. The bigger one injured me and continued to fight with Nahom while Princess Emara held a spear to my throat until I understood who she was. Then the bigger man and Nahom disappeared, and Princess Emara told the other soldiers to look for them. She dressed my wound, and we started for the city. The rest you know. I didn't know it was your sister."

Enon cringes inside at his words but accepts the report. "How is your arm?"

"I must keep it clean and dry and return daily for dressing changes, but it'll heal."

Enon nods. "I hope it'll be a good reminder to use your training rather than let fear get the better of you." He turns to join the search party, leaving the soldier to ponder his words. While he walks, he mulls over what was reported to him. "So many different scenarios could have been used to prevent what just occurred," he mutters under his breath. He shakes his head, wiping away the frown with a determined face. "Now we have to find them." He takes a breath, focusing on the task, and joins Loyola to find out what has been done thus far and what still needs to be accomplished.

Loyola acknowledges Enon with a nod. "How is Emara?"

"Unconscious."

"What? I was just talking to her. We both were."

"She fainted in my arms and hasn't woken up. Mother is with her, and I was dismissed." He sighs. "Right now I need to keep my mind occupied."

Loyola nods. "We have people on ropes who are currently checking the cliff to see if they might still be there. I have sent riders down to the water's edge below the waterfall, which is a half day's ride away from the city. Once done here, I will join them there."

"I'll go with you."

Enon and Loyola do what they can to assist the rescue operation. No men are found by the rescue party dangling off the cliff face. Loyola and Enon are given horses packed with supplies and ride out soon thereafter.

Others in the infirmary offer to tend Emara so the queen can rest, but she refuses and continues to nurse her daughter back to health. She speaks to Emara at regular intervals throughout the night, telling her when to swallow the small drink of broth and reminding her that she needs to wake up.

Emara dreams of Suyana talking to her on a warm summer day. She doesn't know what the conversation is, but it is pleasant and encouraging to hear her mother's voice. The dream changes to walking hand in hand with Ammon and how nice that felt, but then he disappears. She cries out, remembering what happened and struggling for consciousness. She hears a scream and opens her eyes, agitated.

"Emara!" The queen holds her daughter's shoulders down, trying to get her daughter's attention while others come to assist. "Emara. I am here, dear. Stop fighting me."

Emara continues to fight and then registers that someone is speaking to her. Emara blinks a few times as comprehension reaches her brain that in front of her is the face of—

"Mother."

"I am so glad to see you coherent." Suyana smiles at Emara. She removes Emara's hands from her shoulders and grabs her daughter's hand while sitting on the side of the bed.

"Who screamed?"

"You, dear."

"Ammon, he's gone. He . . . he . . . fell off the cliff."

"Enon and Loyola are searching for them. Keep hope alive."

Emara takes a deep breath and blows it out, trying to get her emotions under control. "Where am I?"

"The infirmary. You are quite dehydrated. Would you like a drink?" Emara nods. Suyana feeds Emara several small spoonfuls of broth. "That is enough for now. We need to make sure you can keep that down. I will give you more in a little while." The queen gets off the bed and strokes her daughter's forehead. "Right now, I want you to rest." Emara closes her eyes, hoping that Ammon is still alive.

The next few days, Emara is supervised by her mother. She is fed lots and lots of fluids and told to rest. "It's been three days since I have become conscious. Mother, may I please have some fruit, squash, corn, something other than water and broth, which I am completely tired of drinking? I am sitting up, I can walk around, and I can even take care of my personal needs. My stomach wants real food, and I am tired of being confined to the infirmary."

Suyana chuckles. "It is good to see you are back to normal. I will add to your diet, and if you can tolerate the food well, perhaps tomorrow you can be dismissed from the infirmary." The queen smiles mischievously, whispering, "I will go see about some food before we hear your stomach growl."

Emara breathes a sigh of relief. "Thank you, Mother." Suyana walks away. While the queen is gone, Emara closes her eyes, thinking of Ammon and hoping that word will arrive soon. Suyana comes back a little while later with a cut prickly pear for Emara. Emara smiles her pleasure and begins to suck on the fruit. While Emara is enjoying the prickly pear, a man is brought into the infirmary. After hearing it is some soldier named Nahom, Emara tries to ignore the commotion. She hears something about a leg injury but tries not to eavesdrop and to allow the man some privacy. She notices that people are standing at the foot of her bed and looks up mid-bite to see Enon and Pagog standing there looking sullen.

"It's good to see you are well, Emara." Enon clears his throat and continues, now devoid of emotion. "We found the soldier who was fighting Ammon. His name is Nahom, and he will be in the infirmary with you. Pagog wanted to come and speak with you." Enon nods to the man, and Pagog takes a step forward.

"I want to say I'm sorry, Princess Emara. I hope you will one day forgive me." Pagog looks up at Emara.

Emara's face registers surprise, then the silence between them grows as they look at one another. Enon clears his throat, thrusting Emara toward a response. "Thank you, Pagog." Pagog nods and leaves. Emara turns her attention toward her brother. "What about Ammon?"

Enon looks at her directly. "We haven't found him, but Loyola is still searching." Enon sees his sister's face contort into a multitude of emotions, and tears come to her eyes. The fruit forgotten, she purposefully gets out of bed and walks toward the door.

Enon grabs her by the arm. "What are you doing?"

"I'm leaving. I can't stay in this room with *him*."

He nods his head and leads the way out the door. With Emara walking outside in her nightdress, Enon quickly moves her toward the area for women.

"Why are you helping me? Mother will be furious."

"Because I'm furious with those men. I understand mistakes, but they were going to kill my sister, and now you're hurting because of their actions." Enon pulls her along.

Alma, one of the Arnac women assigned to Emara's quarters, happens to see her, and her face lights up as she comes toward them. "Hi, Emara. Why are you outside in a nightdress?"

"Because she's escaping the infirmary. Take her to her quarters. Not the infirmary." Alma nods open-mouthed as Enon turns to Emara. "I'll take care of Mother." He gives her a quick hug and walks in the opposite direction. Emara, knowing how to get to her quarters, continues forward toward her room without slowing while Alma follows trying to keep up with Emara's quick steps.

GRIEF

EMARA ARRIVES TO HER ROOM and walks directly into the water room. Alma, confused by her demeanor, follows her only to be yelled at. "Get out of here. I want to be alone."

Alma, shocked by Emara's bizarre behavior, goes to find her mother. Emara, unable to contain her emotions any longer, grabs the nearest thing she can find—a towel—and throws it across the room. It falls to the floor not far from her feet. She screams, releasing some of her pent-up emotions. Sorrow and anger engulf her, and she falls to the floor, sobbing until there are no more tears. Emotionally exhausted, she lies there until two gentle hands touch her shoulder to help her sit up. Looking up, she finds it's her mother, who sits herself next to Emara and wraps her in her arms.

"Why, Mother? Why did this have to happen?"

Suyana soothingly strokes her daughter's hair. "They're still searching for him."

"If they find him, I am going to yell at him for making me feel this way."

"I know, dearest."

"I'm so angry right now." Emara hiccups. "I'm angry with the soldiers. If they wouldn't have attacked, Ammon would be here at Arnac. I'm even angry with Ammon and I don't know why. I . . . I . . . I am lost without him. I can't be kind right now. I have nothing left to give. I'm broken inside."

Suyana continues to soothe her daughter, allowing Emara to cry it all out and finally fall asleep with her head on her mother's lap. Suyana sits there with silent tears running down her cheeks and an arm around her daughter as she continues to sleep.

Sometime later, Alma peeks cautiously in to see if she can do anything. She sees Queen Suyana sitting on the floor with her back leaned against the wall, her eyes closed, and her arm wrapped around Emara's shoulder. Emara's head still rests on her lap. Hearing the sound of Alma's entrance, Suyana opens her eyes, sees Alma standing in the doorway, and motions her over. "Emara is going to be well, but it is going to take time. Ask Calene if Enon is still in Arnac. If he is still in Arnac, is there a way for him to be permitted to come here to help me with Emara? Please let her know to inform us at once when Loyola or Ammon returns." Alma nods. "Can you plan for a meal to be brought here? We will need plenty of fluids as well. Thank you, Alma."

Alma nods, stepping out of the room to perform the tasks while Suyana closes her eyes, returning to ideas on how to best help Emara.

Because men aren't allowed to see the city of women, Enon arrives blindfolded with Alma and Orihah helping him into the queen and Emara's quarters. When Enon is told to take off his blindfold, he does so, and Alma puts her finger over her mouth to silence him before he speaks, motioning for him to follow her. Arriving in the water room, he sees his mother sitting on the floor with Emara. He goes to her, worried that Emara is unconscious again.

Seeing the question on his shocked face, Suyana shakes her head. "She is sleeping. Help me get her to bed." Between the two of them, they wake up Emara enough to get her standing and walk her to the bed, where she quickly falls back asleep. The queen, Enon, Orihah, and Alma go into the main area to talk. "Thank you, Orihah and Alma. When will the food be here?"

"If you wish, Orihah and I will leave now to go get it. There are guards posted outside to ensure that Enon does not see the city. He is to remain with you, and when you are done with him, we will help him back to the courtyard."

"Two more chairs would be helpful." Alma nods. "Please give Calene my thanks for this gift, and thank you for all your help." Alma and Orihah leave to get the food and chairs while Enon sits at the table waiting to hear more about Emara. Once Alma and Orihah have left, Suyana turns to her son. "Were you able to find any sign of Ammon?"

"Nothing. What of Emara?"

"She is grieving. She found a man she would like as her husband only to have it ripped away. I suspect she loves Ammon deeply."

"I know if anything happened to Loyola, I would have a hard time dealing with that."

Mother nods. "She is also very angry."

"I am too. How can we help her?"

"It will take time, and right now we need to make sure she eats and drinks and stays safe. She needs to be around people she loves. She might lash out, but we are to remain her constants. Understand?"

"Yes. We're to be here for her."

Mother nods. "I sure hope Loyola finds him."

"Me too. I would like to get to know him better, since Loyola is very fond of Ammon and Emara is interested in him."

They continue talking with one another quietly while Emara sleeps. When the food arrives, it is arranged on the table and the chairs are added. There are strawberries, blueberries, beans, carrots, potatoes, corn flatbread, and different varieties of squash. Mother places an assortment of easy-to-eat foods on Emara's plate and places a cup of water to drink where she will sit Emara. Suyana goes and wakes Emara up, making her get out of bed and come to the table to eat.

Emara sees Enon there. "Why are you here? I thought you were going back to continue the search?"

"I had a change of plans."

"I don't understand. Men are not to be in this part of the city."

"We bent the rules a little bit, Emara," Suyana says. "You are still healing, and I cannot care for you by myself, so Enon has joined us here to help."

"I'm not an invalid, Mother."

"No, you are not. You have been deeply hurt, and we are here to help. Sit down, dear. Would you like a drink of water?" Suyana motions to the seat beside her and the water in a cup, and Emara quickly takes a seat drinking some water.

"Why are you here in Arnac?" Emara asks Enon.

"Mother sent word that Xenu was attacked, so Father sent me back with half the army. He wanted to come himself, but we talked him out of it so he can concentrate on preparing the city for war. I've already sent word back that you and Mother are safe."

Emara's stomach announces itself, and Enon and Suyana look at each other knowingly while Emara takes another drink of water. When Emara is done drinking, she looks at the plate of food in front of her.

"You were saying earlier that you needed other foods, so here you go. See what tastes good to you."

Emara's stomach roars again, and she sighs. She starts trying the different foods while the queen dishes some food out for Enon and herself.

"Mmmm, Emara, have you tried this one?" Enon points at the food he just tried. "It's really good. What do you think about it?"

Emara takes a bite and answers his question, and Suyana joins the ruse. "This is really good. I wonder what ingredients are in it?"

"Is it juniper?"

"No, Enon, its tarragon."

"Oh, didn't know that."

Between her mother and brother, Emara eats half the food on her plate and drinks two cups of water. Emara states she is full, and Suyana dismisses her from the table and helps her back to the bed, where she quickly falls back asleep. Returning to the table, Enon and Suyana continue to talk while they eat.

Later in the day, Emara wakes up from her nap and finds herself alone. She goes to her belongings and pulls out Ammon's necklace. Tears fall from her puffy red eyes as she thinks about Ammon. Taking a breath, she wipes away the tears and decides to wear his necklace.

For the next four days around the clock, they nurse Emara, making sure to keep her mind positive and her body well fed. Nothing is said about the necklace around her throat. They play games like they did at home when it rained all day, and they talk about all sorts of things, trying to help Emara remember happier times. When Emara is ready to share her feelings, Enon and Suyana listen, allowing her to vent. The queen has activities brought in that require the three of them to use their talents to make something useful. "Everyone is to do something positive." Enon intentionally makes something outlandish in an effort to make his sister laugh.

Today, Enon pulls Mother aside. "I am concerned about Loyola. There has been no word."

"Are you asking for permission to leave?" Enon nods. "Emara is in a better place now. Thank you for your help. Now, go get us some answers." Enon nods, squeezing his mother's hand gently, then moves over to Emara and kneels down to be at eye level with her.

"Emmy, it's time for me to go."

Emara looks at him. "Why?"

"I need to find Loyola. Will you help me to the courtyard?"

She looks at him for a moment. "Yes." Once Suyana places the blindfold, Emara opens the door, and the queen and Emara help Enon to the courtyard accompanied by guards.

"You can remove the blindfold now."

Enon removes the blindfold and blinks several times as his eyes adjust to the sunlight. "Thanks, Mother."

"Bring back word about Ammon." Enon nods to Emara. He gives Suyana and Emara a quick hug, then turns and jogs to where the horses are kept, intent on finding Loyola. Emara and Suyana return to their rooms arm in arm, then both continue their sewing project.

"I hope he finds Loyola and that she's found Ammon."

"I am sure that is his intent."

"I hope Ammon is well."

"I hope so too, dear."

"When were you going to tell me that my Joining was arranged?"

Suyana quickly looks up from her sewing project. "Who told you that your husband was arranged?"

"Ammon did. We had an argument, and he told me, but I want to hear it from you." The room remains silent as Emara looks pointedly at her mother. Suyana slowly puts down her sewing project, giving all her attention to her daughter.

"Emara, we are friends with Ammon's parents, and it was arranged in your infancy. Ammon came and visited many years ago when you were still small and made a deal with your father requiring no one to tell you about the arrangement, and we have kept our word."

"But why didn't he want me to know?"

"Because, dear, as young as he was, he wanted you to choose him for his character and not because of his position. I see that is the case?" Suyana motions to the necklace.

Emara touches the necklace at her throat. "Yes, I choose him."

"So if he returns you will choose the Joining instead of the Challenge?"

"I choose him even though there are still unanswered questions for me. It's hard to be without him."

"Dear, I would so love to take away your pain, but perhaps I can help answer any questions you have."

"What is his position?"

"His parents are the king and queen of Xenu, and he is next to be king of Xenu. Helam and Loyola's arranged Joining would provide her with the same opportunity as you, but it did not happen. I haven't had a chance to talk to Loyola about it, but I have talked with Calene. Calene says she was happy it did not occur, and I am glad that things worked out between Loyola and Enon."

"Loyola and Enon? What are you talking about?"

"Loyola has accepted Enon. She wears his necklace."

"I didn't even notice."

"You had other things on your mind at the time."

"When will they be joined?"

"They haven't said, but I think they were waiting for your return."

"When I join Ammon, I will live at Xenu, and I am going to miss you all so much. How am I going to get along without my family?"

"I am going to miss you too, but you will have a new mother, Ammon's mother, who will be there to guide you. She is a good woman, and she will love you as I love you. We can keep in contact through letters, and I want to hear everything. Perhaps your brothers can come and visit every so often. Joining with Ammon is not an end, but the beginning of a new adventure." Suyana smiles at Emara.

Suyana answers as many questions as she can while they continue sewing. Later in the day there is a knock on the door, and Alma answers the door to reveal Calene and Loyola. Emara, seeing Loyola standing in the doorway, drops what she's working on and runs to give Loyola a hug, then ushers both guests into the room. They all sit around the table, and Queen Suyana turns to Loyola. "Did you see Enon? He went in search for you."

"I met Enon on the road and we traveled back together, but he's staying in the courtyard unless you need him."

"Did you find Ammon?"

Loyola looks at Emara for a minute. "No, I found no sign of Ammon." Seeing the change in Emara's countenance and the tears in her eyes, Loyola quickly adds, "Let me explain further. If Ammon were dead, we would have found a body or the remains of one. The fact that we have found nothing means that he may still be alive but perhaps on the opposite bank of the river—somewhere." Loyola grabs Emara's hands that are folded tightly together on the table. "Don't give up hope, Emara. I haven't."

"Loyola is correct," Calene says. "Keep hope alive, and miracles can occur. There is one week left here, and then it will be time to return to Uthal. Emara, your mother told me you plan to take the Challenge. If that is the case, you are welcome to return here."

Emara's countenance brightens. "Thank you, Loyola for bringing me word. I know this is not easy for you either. Thank you, Calene. If Ammon doesn't return, I would like that very much." Turning to her friend again, she says, "Loyola . . . Enon came and stayed with us for the last several days. I wonder if . . . you would be willing to come and stay here with us until we leave."

On their way back to Arnac, Enon filled Loyola in regarding Emara's welfare. "I would love that. Let me bathe and get some supplies, and I'll be back shortly."

The four women continue to talk for a little bit longer, then Calene gets up, announcing her departure, and Loyola follows her out the door.

Emara turns to her mother. "Loyola still has hope."

"Yes, she does." Suyana smiles back. "It will be good to have her here, and while she is here I will take Enon's bed. She can take my bed so you girls can talk."

A clean Loyola returns with some supplies a little while later. Emara explains the setup, and Loyola listens carefully. "Can we go to your favorite spot?" Emara asks.

"We can go if it's all right with your mother."

The queen hears the exchange and nods to Loyola, and the two girls travel out the door.

Under the tree next to the pool of water, Loyola and Emara

sit quietly immersed in their own thoughts while Emara's hands play with the end of her braid. Emara breaks the silence first. "Do you really think Ammon is alive?"

"I have no reason to think otherwise. When he returns, are you going to accept him as your husband?"

"Yes, but I still have some unanswered questions that bother me."

"What are you concerned about?"

Emara laughs slightly. "You're going to think it's stupid."

"If it concerns you, then it's not stupid." Loyola gives Emara her whole attention.

"I know you and Ammon, but I don't know your parents." Emara starts off. "I don't . . . I don't know if I will be accepted. I don't know if I will fit in with your family."

Loyola looks at Emara for a minute. "Your parents are like my parents, and I think my parents allow a little more freedom." Loyola grins at Emara. "They will take you as their daughter."

"What will I do there?"

"Anything you would like to do."

"What will be my place? Currently, I am Emara, a princess, and have to act accordingly."

Loyola nods, finally understanding what is bothering Emara. She thinks for a moment and answers very seriously. "You have a very serious problem." Emara's eyes widen as she looks at Loyola for some clarification. "If you marry Ammon, you will be crown princess, Emara." Loyola grins at Emara. As realization dawns in Emara's head, both girls start laughing. "Nothing is going to change. You'll still do what you've been trained to do." Loyola finishes between the laughter, and a weight lifts from Emara's shoulders.

"Make my brother happy."

"I intend to." The girls sit listening to the waterfall. "How did you meet Enon?"

Loyola looks out across the pond. She has been wearing Enon's necklace for several weeks now. "After leaving you in Ammon's care, we started back toward Arnac and joined the men of Xenu hunting the robbers on our way. Before Arnac, we met up with Enon's army. At first there was tension because we both didn't know one another. When I heard Enon's name, I came forward, introducing myself, and explained how I know both you and your mother. Enon was surprised, and he asked us what we were doing, so I told him. Enon's army joined us, flushing out what we hope to be the remainder of the Gadianton robbers. When the job was finished, I joined Enon's army back to Arnac while Ammon's troops went home to report to my father."

Emara digested the information. "What made Enon interested in you?"

Loyola looks pointedly at Emara and laughs out loud. "I don't know. You'll have to ask him that question."

"Do you love Enon?"

"Yes, otherwise I wouldn't have accepted the necklace."

"I'm glad he found someone to make him happy." Emara smiles at Loyola. They continue talking until Emara's stomach starts announcing itself, which makes them laugh and sends them back to their quarters to eat. When they arrive, Queen Suyana notices that Emara's countenance looks happier.

HOME

Once Loyola and Selina were introduced to each other, they quickly become friends and joined Emara on all her activities, and Suyana breathes a sigh of relief to see that Emara is smiling again. The last week goes by quickly as the threesome joins the others in the hall to eat and in the remaining classes.

The last night in Arnac is another banquet where the men join the women in the hall for dinner. Queen Suyana is seated next to Calene on one side, and Loyola is seated on the other side. Enon is next to Loyola, and Emara is seated next to their mother. After dinner is finished, Calene speaks. "Women of Uthal, tomorrow we part. Blessings to each of you, as you have shown your courage and strength during this difficult time. Tonight is a time to celebrate womanhood, and tomorrow you return home as women."

The music and festival start, and after a while Enon comes and sits next to Emara. "Are you happy?"

"I'm as happy as I can be under the circumstances. Are you happy with Loyola?"

"Yes, I'm happy with her."

"What attracted you to her?"

"She's independent and knows her mind." After a moment he continues. "Just like you, Emmy. Stay that way."

"When will you become her husband?"

"It will happen after the Challenge."

"Enon, no. I can't keep you from Loyola."

"You aren't keeping me from anything. It's how we want it to be. My understanding is you want to return here. Is that still the case?" Emara nods. "Loyola and I will bring you back, and once that is done, then I will be her husband."

"I want to be there for that."

"You will be there for that." Enon returns winking, bringing a smile to Emara's face. "If Ammon returns, will you accept him as your husband?"

"Yes."

"Does he make you happy, Emmy?"

"Yes, he does. We work very well together."

"That is good. I hope you'll invite us to your Joining, because we want to be there."

"Thank you, Enon. I want you both to be there."

"Good. Loyola is going to sleep in her own quarters tonight, as she needs to finish packing things up before tomorrow." Emara nods and Enon squeezes her hand before returning to Loyola's side.

Calene watches the festivities from her chair with a smile on her face, and after a little while Queen Suyana, Abish, and Calene are deep in conversation. Emara and Selina find their friends saying goodbyes and talking with those they know who are staying in Arnac. After some time, Emara sits next to her mother, who says, "Calene, we are returning to our quarters for the night." Calene nods, dismissing them.

Mother and daughter walk quietly to the cemetery to visit Limhi's grave, and Suyana stands back, allowing her daughter time at the grave mound.

"Limhi, I know you have moved on to a better place, but I miss your conversation and stories." A tear drops from her eye and she quickly brushes it away, pausing before she continues. "I have met a man that I hope will return to me and be my husband. His name is Ammon, and I miss him terribly. He is such a good man, and I think you would like him and be friends. I hope to be joined to him when he returns." Emara takes a deep breath. "I'm sure your family misses you, and when I see them, I will do my best to convey your love for them. Thank you for trying to protect me. Thank you for your friendship." Emara stands there quietly. "My life changed for the better after knowing you. I shall visit you again soon, since I'm returning to Arnac. I love you and look forward to seeing you in the afterlife." She wipes away another tear, getting her emotions under control before she nods to her mother. Mother comes forward and wraps a comforting arm around Emara, and they walk quietly to their room.

It's just Suyana and Emara in the room, sitting at the table and reminiscing about the last four moons. Emara shares her time with Ammon during her recovery and her walk back to Arnac with him. When she finishes telling her story, Suyana asks, "What helped you the most in dealing with your anger?"

"Loyola told me early on when we arrived at Arnac that there are three types of challenges we face: ones we give ourselves, ones others give us through their choices, and ones that just happen. I've experienced all of these during the last four moons. I have learned that I cannot control what happens, but I can control how I act. After Loyola returned from looking for Ammon, I asked her why she was not angry and still had hope. She explained to me that anger and bad feelings toward others only hurt the person who keeps them and lets them fester like an infection. I think she knew that both Enon and I were struggling with anger issues. I finally understood that I had to forgive so I could move forward again. Once I understood that, I asked her how to do that and she told me it was through service. To help me forgive, Loyola suggested we start with those I was most angry at. So Selina, Loyola, and I went and visited Nahom in the infirmary, spending some time with him while he recovered. I discovered that he is a good man who made a mistake and regrets it. We also visited Pagog, and again I discovered that he is a good man who also regrets his mistake. Both of them told us how sorry they were for their actions and have scars as a reminder. I don't know exactly when, but I was finally able to let the anger go, and one day I just noticed that the anger was gone."

"That is good. Loyola is correct that anger and bad feelings only hurt the person who harbors them. I am glad that Loyola was there when you were ready to hear it. Service can heal many problems, including a broken heart."

"I'm very grateful that you and Enon were there to help me when I couldn't look beyond my pain. I'm sorry if I wasn't pleasant to be around and not thinking clearly."

Suyana gets up from her chair and comes around the table, indicating that her daughter should stand up. Emara instinctively follows her mother's instructions, and Suyana enfolds her daughter in a loving embrace. When she releases her daughter, she takes Emara's hands and looks in her eyes. "You have nothing to be sorry for. I love you, Emara, and am so thankful that I was able to be here with you. I think your brother feels the same." Giving her daughter another hug, she places the turquoise stone in Emara's hand and pulls back, smiling. "It is late. If we are going to be ready in the morning, we need to get some sleep." She ushers her daughter into the bedroom for the night.

Emara looks at the stone in her hand and says, "This is beautiful. Where did you get it?"

Suyana's head pops up. "From your pack. Do you know what turquoise means?" Emara looks up at her mother and shakes her head. "Turquoise is only given in love and is the most precious of stones. It is a gift from the Great Spirit." They stand there for a moment, thinking of the only other person who would have access to her pack—Ammon. That night Emara dreams of him and his kiss, but the dream changes to Ammon struggling to survive.

The next morning Emara is shaken awake by the queen. At first, Emara lowers her eyes as she struggles to hide her tender heart full of both loss and hope for Ammon. There is a flurry of activity around her as mother instructs Alma and Orihah to pack things, and soon Emara is able to move those feelings to the back of her mind, focusing on the task at hand. Suyana and Emara take their traveling clothes into the bathing area and quickly dress, then take one last look around the rooms to make sure they have gathered everything to the front door to be taken to their horses.

"Do you have everything?"

"I think so."

"Then it is time to say goodbye." Suyana takes the lead walking to Orihah and Alma. "Thank you, Orihah. Thank you, Alma. Both of you have taken such good care of us."

"Here is a little something for you." Emara hands a gift to Orihah and one to Alma, watching as they unwrap them.

"It is beautiful, Emara. Thank you so much for the belt." Alma gives Emara a hug.

"I will treasure it always." Orihah twirls around, showing

off the embroidered scarf, then gives Emara a hug. "When did you have time to make it?"

"While Mother was taking care of me, I thought of the both of you. Thank you for everything you have done during our stay here."

"We will miss you."

"Not for long, as I'm planning on returning." Orihah and Alma squeal happily hugging Emara again. After one final hug, Suyana and her daughter leave their quarters, rushing over to the hall to get a good breakfast before their departure. In the hall, they sit in the seats next to Calene, while Loyola is on the other side. Selina sits across from Emara, talking to her about the long trip home, and moments later the food is served and everyone eats. After eating, the women mingle, saying last-minute farewells, until Calene gives the nod that it's time to leave. Calene and the queen lead the women out to the courtyard, where they find their horses and gear ready for travel. Queen Suyana pulls a container out of her pocket. "Calene, this is a gift from Emara and myself." She passes the container to Calene, who lifts her eyebrows in surprise at the present. "It is ginseng, a rare herb that Emara found traveling back to Arnac." They continue to talk for a minute as Suyana explains how to use it.

Calene takes the treasured gift, dropping it in her pocket. "Suyana, blessings of much joy and happiness, with many grandchildren to keep you occupied."

Suyana laughs and grins. "Blessings of vitality, health, and happiness."

Calene nods to Suyana and then turns to Emara. "I will see you soon."

The queen and her daughter walk to their horses and mount. While the rest of the women say their goodbyes and get ready to depart, Loyola gives Calene a hug, whispering something in her ear, and Calene smiles. Loyola walks to where her horse stands, near Suyana and Emara, and turns, taking a final look back at Calene before climbing up. Each of the women is now armed and has her weapons within easy reach should she need them during the journey home.

Enon, on his horse, watching patiently from a distance with the men by the gate, has Omni next to him. When everyone is ready, Enon brings the guard to Queen Suyana. "Mother. Emara. You probably already know Omni well since he is one of the guards who brought you to Arnac and over-saw the men while stationed here. He'll now lead the women back to Uthal. He has twice as many guards as you had when you left for Arnac. The army has already left, and you'll fol-low, but we'll keep both groups separated." The queen nods. The gates are opened, and the company moves out. But the women recall the attack that happened almost four moons ago and are watchful.

"We're on our way home, and in seven sunrises, I will be joined to Helam. I'm so excited." Selina continues to talk nonstop to Emara and Loyola, who listen to her excited chatter as they move down the mountain while Abish and Suyana talk among themselves ahead of them.

On their way, Emara notices the clearing next to the river where the first attack took place and finds herself moving her horse toward it. Loyola comes with her while Selina informs the queen. Emara allows her horse to drink as she looks up and down the river's edge for any sign of Ammon and thinks of her friend, Limhi, and how his life ended here.

"Emara, he's not here. It's time to leave." Emara nods her head, and they both head back to the group continuing down the mountain. When they reach the bottom of the mountain, Omni informs them of their responsibilities just like the previous leader. Guards are set around the parameter while chores are completed. Horses are fed and watered while kindling is gathered. Dinner is cooked while tents are erected.

The group eats around the fire, many talking about their plans when they get back, especially Selina. After dinner and the remaining chores are completed, Suyana, Loyola, and Emara head to their tents, which are next to one another.

Suyana says, "Loyola, gather your belongings. Emara and you will share that tent while I take the other." Loyola looks at Suyana for a minute then nods. When everything is rearranged and after Emara and Loyola get settled, Suyana gives her daughters a hug and departs to her new sleeping quarters.

Out of the darkness, Loyola says, "You've been quiet all day. What's bothering you?"

"Mother gave me a turquoise stone last night and stated she found it in my pack. I didn't find the stone. I think Ammon put it there before . . . I dreamed he was struggling all night. I'm worried about him."

"There isn't much we can do if we don't know where he is. He has the skills to find his way back to Arnac, and he'll get there. The best thing we can do now is to have hope."

"My heart aches for him."

"I know it does. Sleep, Emara. We have a task at hand, and if we concentrate on that, there will be no time for sadness."

The next morning arrives quickly, and everyone is up, excited, and on task to begin the day's journey toward home.

Selina says, "Six sunrises before Helam and I are bound. I can't wait."

Before long Omni stops the group and rides back to inform the queen that there are some rocks in the shape of a pyramid in the path. "This is the way Enon communicates to those following." The queen, Emara, and Loyola follow Omni to the pyramid-shaped rocks. Taking off the top rock, Omni finds two small parchments of paper with one addressed to him and one addressed to Loyola. Omni reads his first. "Go until you find the pyramid and camp there."

He turns to Loyola, who opens her message and reads it silently first with a smile touching her mouth. When she is done reading, she looks up and says, "It's a personal message that I'll receive daily." Omni breaks the mound of rocks with his foot, and travel resumes.

"Why did we stop?" Selina asks.

Loyola looks at Selina, "Enon left a message."

"What was the message?"

"To continue to the next message point."

"Is that it? Was there anything else?"

"No."

Emara shoots a look at Loyola, who reveals nothing in response Selina's questions. As they continue, the conversation turns to something other than Selina's upcoming plans, and Loyola and Emara are grateful for the new subject. Later in the day, Suyana and Abish call Selina up to talk with them. Loyola and Emara grin at each other, knowing that they are talking about Selina accepting Helam as her husband, and they are glad they are not part of it.

"I know why you kept Enon's message to you private." Loyola looks at Emara. "You are correct. If Selina knew about it, she would pester until she knew what the message said."

"Thank you for understanding." They ride together, enjoying the silence.

Omni stops the group again as he fetches the next messages. After reading his message, he brings back the one for Loyola and hands it to her. In a loud voice, Omni bellows, "We are stopping here for the night. There is a well nearby, and Prince Enon has left us some food to cook. You know your chores, so get to work and set up camp."

Each day continues with little messages, and Loyola keeps her messages to herself. The queen and Emara do not pry, knowing that those messages are special to her. As the days progress, Suyana and Abish spend more time talking with Selina, and time seems to pass quickly on their journey home. Tomorrow, they reach Uthal.

THE CHOICE

MORNING DAWNS WITH EXCITEMENT AS everyone spends extra time making sure that each woman looks presentable. Loyola helps Emara with her hair, and Emara does the same for Loyola. They're tired of traveling and look forward to being clean again. "Tonight, you sleep in my home, Loyola, where we have a soft bed and private room for you. Thank you for traveling with me."

"The trip is not over for us. Tomorrow we'll be doing this again as we travel back to Arnac."

"You had to remind me. I'm not happy about saying good-bye to my family."

"I know. Enon and I will be with you. You're not going alone."

"I bet it was very difficult for you when you left your family."

"It was, but I had Ammon, which helped a lot. When I got to Arnac, I then had my aunt, who took me in as her daughter. I can't imagine someone taking the Challenge without support."

"Enon introduced me to a lady named Ziva before the Journey. She had no other siblings and took the Challenge with her best friend as guardian. She had a difficult challenge but survived, but her best friend did not. She joined a man by the name of Lib and now has three beautiful children."

"It takes a lot of courage to take the Challenge, especially without support."

"Do a lot of women take the Challenge in Xenu?"

"No, not at all. What about Uthal?"

"Very rarely does someone take the Challenge, but this year, I will be the one."

Emara finishes fixing Loyola's hair, and Loyola gets up, facing Emara. "And it will be the right choice for you. Thank you for fixing my hair."

"Thank you for styling mine. Let's go find Selina."

Selina is being fussed over by Abish and Suyana. The girls grin at Selina and change course to get some breakfast. They grab a bowl of mush and sit down with the others to eat, listening to the happy chatter as the other women share their plans. Suyana arrives, critically looking over Loyola's and Emara's appearance before nodding her approval. On the other hand, Emara notices her mother's countenance is neat and comely, which causes a frown to crease her brow. Suyana, not noticing Emara's face but satisfied that her daughters are ready for the day, leaves to get some breakfast.

Selina and Abish arrive with bowls of food, joining the company looking radiant. Selina, hardly able to contain herself, squeals "Today I will take Helam as my husband."

"Yes, you will." Emara returns between bites.

"We are happy for you." Loyola smiles at Selina.

"You both will be there?"

"Of course." Emara smiles at her.

"Wouldn't miss it."

"Good, because I need you there." Selina sits down next to Emara.

"Mother needs some help with her appearance. I will find a better shirt and ties."

Loyola looks at Suyana, who is in line for food. "I'll do her hair."

Selina says, "I have flowers that can be used in her hair."

Emara nods to Selina and goes to get the supplies she needs while Suyana returns with a bowl and sits down.

"Where did Emara go?"

Loyola looks at Suyana. "She's gathering some supplies." Abish and Selina stuff their mouths full of food to keep from saying anything more. "Did you sleep well? You look tired."

"I am worried that our husbands may have forgotten something important with regards to today's activities. There is quite a lot going on with the Stand and the Joining." Suyana inserts a spoonful of mush into her mouth, and the women nod in agreement as they continue eating their breakfast.

Loyola watches Emara as she walks around the perimeter of camp to advance to the group behind her mother. Loyola, knowing what Emara is trying to do, lets Emara know when to hold off or to take some steps forward without the queen seeing. When Suyana is done with the contents in her bowl, Selina jumps up. "May I take your bowls to get cleaned?"

Suyana, Abish, and Loyola hand their bowls to her, and Selina, loaded with bowls and spoons, happily heads away in an effort to leave the group to retrieve the flowers while Emara arrives with the supplies. Between the three women, Suyana doesn't know what hit her as she is quickly changed into a new shirt and sat in front of Loyola, who deftly styles her hair, weaving in flowers that Selina brings back.

"How does she look, Abish?"

"She looks like a queen. Loyola, you have quite a talent for styling hair."

"Thank you. I agree with you, Abish. I think she's ready."

"Mother, I think you're ready to greet Father." Emara smiles happily, helping her mother to her feet.

Once camp is packed up, the group heads for the gates of Uthal. Mother and daughter ride side by side. Loyola is riding on the other side of Suyana as one of her daughters. Half the guards lead the group and half follow the women, ensuring their entrance into the city. The gates are open as the group arrives, and the streets are lined with people cheering the women who have returned. Emara is wide-eyed, taking it all in as they follow Omni back to the square. Once at the Stand, they are told to go into the building and await the king to call them out while their horses and supplies are retrieved and returned to the palace to be cared for.

There are three women inside the building whose year is up, and today will be a big day for them as well. The three women are dressed in their best clothes, waiting their turn to be presented, and only one woman has a necklace. This means that if there is not an offer from a man, then the king will decide who will be her husband. Emara knows that her father does not take this responsibility lightly. He has several couples help him find an appropriate man of Joining age. Emara hopes that someone will step forward, or at least her father will provide worthy men who will make the women without a necklace happy. Queen Suyana comes and gives Emara a hug before taking Loyola with her.

"It is time for me to stand on my own," Emara says.

"That it is, dear, and I could not be prouder of who you have become."

"Thank you, Mother."

"Thank you, Loyola for being such a wonderful friend."

Abish gives Selina a hug and departs, following the queen and Loyola, leaving Selina grinning from ear to ear. "It's just us now. Oh, I'm so excited."

Emara can see the concern on two of the three women's faces and moves forward with the desire to say something that will give them hope. Asking their names and introducing herself, she tells them how beautiful they look, and in turn, they thank her. She takes a breath before proceeding, "I don't know if it will help, but my father will do his best to make sure to give you an honorable husband." A tear falls from the eye of one of the women who is without a necklace.

The woman with the necklace looks back at her. "What do you choose—a husband or the Challenge?"

"I choose the Challenge."

"Because you don't want your father to choose for you?"

"Because I'm not ready for a husband. Knowing all the work my father does to make sure he finds a suitable spouse, I would be willing to put my fate in his hands. Again, I am not ready for a husband, so I choose the Challenge and am satisfied with that choice."

"Yet here you are, wearing a necklace."

"And so I am."

Selina unable to keep quiet any longer steps forward. "I will have you know her father did choose her husband, and they both were happy with his choice. Unfortunately, she lost that man. She has been kinder to you than you've been to her." Selina tries pulling Emara away from the three women to stand at the back of the line in preparation for what is about to start. "I think it's time for the Stand to begin."

Emara holds her ground, looking at the three women in front of her. "Thank you Selina, but I can stand for myself." Turning to the two people the message was intended for, she continues kindly, "My words were intended to provide hope to those that need it."

"It didn't work." The woman with the necklace fires back.

Emara turns, looking at the woman with the necklace, smiling politely. "Then the message was not intended for you." Giving the two women the message was intended for a slight nod, Emara turns and walks back to her place at the end of the line, leaving the three women standing there and Selina following after her with a shocked look on her face.

"Wow. Where did that come from? I've never seen you that bold before. That was perfect."

"Selina, they're about to start."

"We'll talk later." Selina smiles and rushes off, taking her place in line.

King Gilgal and Queen Suyana are standing together on the Stand while Helam stands on the other side of Suyana. Gilgal raises his arm to quiet the crowd, and when the crowd is quiet, the king begins. "Thank you to all of you who have come to the Stand today. It is our custom for mothers to spend four moons with their daughters before they decide to choose a spouse or take the Challenge. Four moons ago there were three beautiful women who still did not have a husband. These three women are with us today." The first woman is brought forward, and she is without a necklace. She announces her name, and King Gilgal states, "Who will stand with this woman?"

Two men bow at her feet in hopes they will be chosen, and she is surprised by the response. The woman looks at the face of each suitor and makes up her mind, choosing one of the men. He stands up, takes off his necklace, and presents it to her. The woman takes this necklace and places it around her neck while the other man departs.

Gilgal says, "Parents come forward and greet your children."

The parents of the woman and man come forward and the group exits the Stand.

The woman with the necklace is called forward, and she proudly announces her name. King Gilgal asks, "Who will stand with this woman?" One man comes forward and kneels at her feet, and she nods her head, accepting him. The parents are called, and the group is dismissed.

The last woman, the one earlier with the tear, is called forward and states her name, and Emara watches with bated breath, hoping her father will provide her the correct person for a husband. The king says her name and calls, "Who will stand with this woman?" No one comes forward, and she bows her head humbly. "Be of good cheer. There is a husband for you." The king pats her hand and smiles kindly, calling out the name of the man. Out of the crowd and up the stairs comes a man who looks uncomfortable as he stops and kneels at her feet. She recognizes him as someone she knows and likes, which lights up her face. "Do you accept him?"

"Yes." She shouts joyfully, making Emara smile.

When the man stands up, he smiles happily at the woman's response and gently places the necklace around her neck. The parents are brought forward, and the group leaves the Stand.

"All three couples are required to be joined before nightfall. It is now time to meet the newest women of Uthal." King Gilgal raises an arm toward the new women as they come forth to stand on the platform. When Helam takes each woman by the hand and ushers her forward, she states her name for the city to hear, something about herself, and what she chooses.

Selina's turn comes as she takes Helam's hand and moves forward, radiantly smiling up at him. When he stops, she drops her hand, turning her attention toward the audience.

"My name is Selina, and I am optimistic and loyal. I choose the Joining." Helam returns her to the line, slightly squeezing her hand before moving to the next woman.

After all the other women have had their turn, it is Emara's turn to stand, and each woman that has preceded her has chosen the Joining. Emara takes a breath, blowing it out slowly before placing her hand in Helam's to allow him to move her forward. She sees the rest of her brothers grouped together with Loyola, and Abish is nearby with her family.

"My name is Princess Emara." She swallows. "I am a warrior, and I choose the Challenge."

HOMECOMING

THE CROWD GASPS AT EMARA's choice, and people start talking among themselves. Emara looks to her father, feeling the crowd's negative reaction. King Gilgal puts an arm in the air, indicating the crowd needs to quiet down so he can continue, and he looks at his daughter, smiling proudly. Finally, the rumbling crowd wants to hear from their king. "Each woman has the opportunity to choose, and my daughter has chosen wisely. My family supports her in her decision, which means she will leave Uthal before dawn. The women who have chosen the Joining now have the opportunity to find a husband before we do this again next year." Helam comes forward, smiling at his sister, and escorts Emara back to the line of women.

The king's countenance changes again. "Before we leave the Stand today, some of you have noticed we have missing guards. The Gadianton robbers attacked the women on their way to Arnac." The crowd roars again at the mention of the robbers, and the king holds up his arm, patiently waiting for the city to quiet again. "It is with great sadness that several guards were lost." The throng erupts as news is spread, and Gilgal holds his arm up until the multitude quiets. "If you have not been reunited with a family member, please move forward so that their message may be given."

Queen Suyana steps forward after the crowd adjusts itself and quiets down. "I will call each person's name, then the family is to come to the Stand to meet the messenger. Once all names are called and the Stand is completed, the messages will be given to the family."

Suyana says each person's name and waits for the family to arrive on the platform. Each person who will deliver the message is given two sheep and moves toward the defined group. Limhi's name is called, and Emara steps forward to do her duty. The rope leading the sheep is put in her hand, and she walks forward, fighting tears as she sees the shocked faces of his adopted family.

After the remaining names are called and the messenger comes forward to meet the family, Suyana finishes, "We truly mourn the loss of each of these brave men who have been buried at Arnac cemetery. It is by their sacrifice that these women are here today."

King Gilgal steps forward to stand with Suyana. "Our condolences to those that mourn. Women, you have one year from today to find a husband. Princess Emara will depart Uthal before dawn. The Stand is concluded so that these things can be accomplished." The crowd disperses, leaving those with messages to deliver to the family.

Emara introduces herself to each member of Limhi's family, putting names with faces, and says something to each one of them individually. "Limhi loved you all so much. He was so grateful for your taking him in when he was an orphan and for loving him as your own child. He died defending the women from the Gadianton robbers, but there was nothing I could do to prevent it." A tear falls from one of her eyes, and she quickly brushes it away. Emara hands the sheep to Limhi's father. "These sheep can never replace him." She wipes her eyes before another tear drops, taking a breath before she continues. "He will forever hold a place in my heart as a brother and true friend." The parents give her a hug, then turn to leave as the mother gathers her children's hands and the father leads the sheep away. She stands there with tears coursing down her cheeks as she watches the families depart until it seems to be only her.

Emara's grief is turned to joy when she is unexpectedly engulfed in family hugging her and teasing that she stinks. Most of all she receives a firm, loving hug from her father who looks upon her proudly and gently wipes away her remaining tears. "Very well done. You look beautiful, Emara." Taking a breath to control his emotions, he turns to his family, "We have just today, so let us make the most of it." Emara brushes off the last tear that escaped her eyes as the family turns toward home with the guards accompanying them.

FAMILY

ONCE HOME, MOTHER AND DAUGHTER take Loyola to Emara's room to pick out a clean dress, then Suyana continues to her room to get a change of clothes. "I know it is not one of your dresses, but it is clean. Take your pick, Loyola." Emara shows her wardrobe. "Selina is going to be furious if we do not show up soon to help her get ready."

"I am sure Abish and Selina are bathing before the ceremony, so we have a little time."

"The way my brothers have teased me, I bet we look better than we smell."

"Even with the stench, they still gave you big hugs welcoming you home. You have a good family, Emara. I'm glad to be included in it."

"Why don't you accept Enon today as your husband?"

"And take away Selina's day? She would be furious with me."

Realizing that Loyola is correct, Emara grins. "That she would."

"No, I will wait until you are settled at Arnac. We're going to stick to the plan." Loyola pulls out a dress, holding it up to her body. "How do you think this dress will look?"

"Not as beautiful as the person wearing it, but I think it will do nicely." Emara takes her turn rummaging through her wardrobe and finds a sage-green dress to wear.

"Girls, we need to hurry."

Loyola and Emara look up to see Suyana in the doorway and look at each other, grinning, before following Queen Suyana to the bathing hut. When they get there, they see an assortment of women ready to help the queen and her daughters get the smell off, clean up, and dress for the Joining.

They return to the main house later smelling clean and looking beautiful, arriving to find Helam dressed and pacing the floor, anxious to go to Selina's home—making the women smile.

Emara asks, "Where are you going to live?"

"There is another building here that is for the crown prince that Father and Mother lived in when they were first joined. I have updated it so it will be presentable for Selina. I hope she likes it."

"May we see it before we go to Selina's?"

"Quickly. I would like to get this over with."

Suyana and Gilgal grin at one another, following Helam and the rest of the family to the small rectangular home made of sturdy wood next to the palace. Helam shows to the women the inside of the small home, which contains three rooms. The main room has painted mural walls with vibrant rugs and pottery on a table in the corner. The other rooms are bedrooms with colorful bedding.

When the women return from investigating the house, Gilgal puts an arm around Suyana. "Helam and Selina will eat with the family in the palace and therefore will not need a kitchen nor a water room."

"It looks beautiful."

"You did well, son. "

Emara nudges Helam's shoulder. "I think Selina will like it."

"I agree." Loyola smiles.

"Good. Can we go now?"

"A little excited?"

"I have to do something." Telah dashes out the door.

"Nervous?" Hezekiah grins.

"Not at all," Helam returns, elbowing his brother on the way out of the house. The family waits there for Telah, which prompts Helam to start pacing again. Finally, Telah returns, and Helam confronts him. "Where did you go?"

"I had to release my waste."

Gilgal and Suyana chuckle, enjoying their children's antics, which leads to Gilgal kissing Suyana on the forehead. "After tonight it will never be this way again."

The children follow behind their parents as they lead the way to Selina's home. Loyola and Emara walk behind the brothers, who continue to tease Helam. The guards accompany them, making sure they are safe.

They arrive at Selina's home, where all males have been deposited outside the dwelling by the women in the family. The men are to converse with friends and relatives who are not permitted inside Abish's home. Within the house only the bride, the mothers of bride and groom, grandmothers of bride and groom, and females involved in the ceremony are allowed. Outside, a sheep is cooking while friends of the family prepare other food. Selina's grandmother admits Suyana, Emara, and Loyola into the house, where they find Selina smiling ear to ear. She is clothed in a new, brightly colored dress, with stockings and new shoes. Helam's necklace completes the ensemble. After paying respects to Selina,

239

Loyola takes over guarding the doorway so the grandmother can arrange Selina's hair.

"Is Helam outside?" Selina asks.

"Yes," Suyana chuckles, "and he is just as excited as you are."

Selina's grandmother intricately braids Selina's hair with quick hands. When Selina's hair is done, Suyana presents her with shell earrings with turquoise accents.

"These are beautiful," Selina says, admiring them in her hands, then looks up at Suyana with shiny eyes. "Thank you." Abish helps place them on her ears. "I think I'm ready."

Abish stands up. "I'm not. Let me look at you." Selina stands up, looking radiant, and Emara and Loyola smile. "Turn around." Selina smiles back, then slowly turns around so her mother can see every angle. "Now I think you are ready." Abish gives her daughter a hug, turning her to her grandmother, who also gives her a hug. Both mothers stand in the doorway, indicating that they are ready for the ceremony to begin. There is a big crowd in the yard, and several individuals get King Gilgal's attention by pointing to the door where the mothers stand. He concludes his conversation, then walks to the front of the house and takes his place near the front door.

Inside, Selina's grandmother stands next to her.

"Oh!" Selina releases grandmother's hand and bounces to something on the table. "I forgot the clothes."

Selina rushes to give Helam's new shirt she lovingly made for this occasion to Emara to hold. To Loyola, she gives Helam's new shoes. Once the task is done, she bounces back to her grandmother, taking her hand once more. Suyana and Abish wait until Selina settles. Once Selina is calm, Suyana and Abish move forward a few feet, revealing the grandmother escorting Selina outside for Helam to see. Emara and Loyola follow and stand next to them, holding the clothing.

"Today is a glorious day for a Joining." Gilgal looks at

Helam's smiling face and then at Selina's face as she glows. "The sun shines brightly, but not as brightly as Selina." The crowd laughs and smiles. "She is beautiful. Who will stand with her?" Helam comes forward, joined by his brothers, and kneels in front of Selina. "A man bows in front of you, Selina, to symbolize he will serve you all his days. He will provide for you and any offspring. He will make you happy, and he will keep you safe. Your name?"

"My name is Helam, crown prince of Uthal."

"You do this of your own free will?"

"Yes, I choose of my own free will."

"Selina, do you accept this man as your husband?"

"Yes."

"Do you do this of your own free will?"

"Yes, I do this of my own free will."

"You may dress your husband."

Emara and Loyola step forward with the clothing. Selina takes off Helam's shirt and dresses him in the new shirt, then Helam bows, allowing Selina access to his feet to change his shoes. Once the shoes are on Helam's feet and Selina has stepped back, the king continues the ceremony. "Selina, you clothed Helam to symbolize that you will take care of his needs and you will make him happy. You will join him and multiply." Father smiles. "Selina, take your husband." Selina walks forward and Helam stands up. Helam removes the bracelet from her left wrist and puts it on her right wrist, symbolizing she is joined. When Helam is done with the bracelet, Helam takes Selina's hand. King Gilgal turns them toward the onlookers. "Friends and family, greet Helam and Selina, who are now joined."

A roar goes up and music starts playing as people crowd around the newly joined couple to offer their congratulations. Gifts are given to the new couple and placed on the porch. Mothers, grandmother, Emara, and Loyola all move to where the meal prep is to oversee and to help. Besides the roasted sheep, there is marinated turkey and smoked fish. Side dishes of beans, corn, squash, and steamed cactus are set up next to the meats. Sliced tomatoes, onions and, cornbread and corn flatbread are available to add to the meal. On another table, an assortment of fruits consisting of blueberries, strawberries, and prickly pears are laid out next to the sweet bread. There is an area where a drink made from corn is freely available to all.

While the meal is being prepared, the fathers gather the young couple and tell stories, dispensing wisdom and advice. First to share their story is the bride's father, Lahonti, who takes Helam by the shoulder. "When I was newly joined, I returned home after a rainy day. I did not remove my muddy shoes before entering the home. Abish chased me outside to sit in the rain until she was done cleaning my mess, then she had me change out of my wet clothes on the porch before she let me inside. For a man who was tired and wet, I learned my lesson not to make more work for my wife." Laughs sound from around the group, as many could relate to his story.

Lahonti sits and Gilgal stands, coming to Helam's side. "When your mother and I were newly joined, I failed to listen to Mother's concerns over a deer that invaded the garden. She brought it up numerous times, but I failed to do anything about it. One night I showed up for dinner and there was no dinner. Being a reasonable man, I asked her why there was no food, and she told me the deer ate it all. That night I went hungry and slept very little. The next morning, as soon as light arrived, the deer was killed and peace was restored within our home. I learned to always listen to my wife's concerns, and since that day, we have not had another deer in the garden." More laughter roars from those listening to the stories.

Helam and Selina listen attentively, hearing the stories from family and neighbors. When the men are done dispensing advice and Abish is ready, the celebration continues with much food and dancing.

Emara looks at Enon and Loyola, grinning. "Next, will be your turn."

They smile at her words, bringing her up to dance with them.

Late at night it is time for Helam to take Selina to her new home. He walks her down the street, holding her arm affectionately while quietly talking with her as the family follows them a few feet behind, followed by friends and neighbors. Music plays as they move through the streets. The couple finally arrive at the palace, where no one but those allowed by the king may continue. He keeps it to just family, and they continue following Helam and Selina up to the doorway of their new home.

Helam and Selina turn, smiling to their family. "Thank you."

Helam grins, then picks up Selina, who squeals while everyone laughs. Helam carries his wife inside while the family sings the Joining song.

Two are now joined,
Making life together, joined as one.
Man serving Woman,
Woman serving Man,
Making life together, joined as one.

After the Joining song, the family leaves the newly joined

couple to themselves by moving the party to the dining area, where more food and drink are available. They talk until the early morning hours. Then Selina's family return to their home, leaving the immediate family smiling but tired, sitting around the table while Enon holds Loyola's hand.

"Enon, from what I can see, you are next to be joined. When will this take place?"

"I made a promise to Emara to take her back to Arnac. Loyola and I will do that, then we will make our plans."

Suyana takes Gilgal's hand. "Do you know where you are going to make your home?"

Loyola shakes her head. "At present, we haven't decided."

"We'll figure it out."

"Enon and Loyola, know that we will be happy to have you settled in Uthal." Gilgal turns to Emara. "Emara, are you happy to be returning to Arnac?"

"I will miss my family greatly, but that is where I need to be."

"Then I do not want to waste a moment sleeping away the time I have left with two of my children." Gilgal clears his throat. "If Ammon returns, what will you do?"

"I will accept him as my husband."

Father nods. "He sounds like he has won my daughter's heart . . . is he worthy of you?"

Emara answers by telling her story of her recovery and traveling with Ammon back to Arnac. When she is done, Father nods.

"Loyola, does my daughter paint an accurate picture of Ammon's character?"

"Yes, he is a good and honest man."

Gilgal nods, turning his attention back to Emara. "What if he does not return?"

"Then I will remain at Arnac."

"Loyola, do your parents know about Enon?"

"I sent a message to them before we left Arnac. I hope there will be a reply waiting for me when I return."

Father's eyes focus on the two men seated at the table who are dozing off. "Hezekiah and Telah, if you would like to get a few hours of sleep before Emara, Enon, and Loyola leave, we will make sure to get you up so you can say goodbye."

"I don't want to go to bed." Telah yawns. "But I can't keep my eyes open anymore."

"Me too." Hezekiah yawns, stretching. Telah and Hezekiah stay at the table, not wanting to miss anything, while Gilgal and Suyana look at each other and chuckle as the two children continue to doze. The conversation turns to lighter things as they recall happy family memories.

Emara looks at her father. "I remember when I was small, Father would put me on his shoulders, and I felt like I was on top of the world."

Suyana starts laughing. "I recall when you were on his shoulders before you were able to control yourself, you had a tendency to void."

"Yes, you did. It would go down my neck." Gilgal looks at his wife as he recalls the memory while laughter rings around the table.

"Mother!"

This turn in the conversation awakens the two dozing boys, and they join the conversation. "I remember that too." Hezekiah stretches, trying to wake himself up. "I loved being on Father's shoulders."

"Me too." Is echoed from the rest of the children.

Enon looks at his mother. "I remember Mother giving us honeycomb to eat on family outings. It was such a wonderful treat." The family chimes in recalling how they felt and how sweet the honeycomb tasted.

Telah stands up and stretches. "I remember family picnics and playing ball. They were such fun times."

"I remember . . ." Suyana starts giggling. "Working in the garden when you children were small, and Enon found a snake. Father picked the snake up, showing it to all of you, and when you were done looking at the snake"—Suyana continues laughing, trying to tell her story—"Father placed the snake in the path of old Fatima. I recall all of you watching for poor old Fatima to cross paths with the snake, which shortly thereafter happened. Fatima threw the load of clean laundry off her head, making it fly through the air while she ran away screaming." Suyana continues laughing, wiping the tears from her eyes. When the laughter dies down around the table, she wipes the remaining tears from her eyes. "I have to admit it was such an unusual sight."

"I think the snake was more afraid of Fatima than she of the snake," Telah says, sitting at the table again. "Do you remember how fast the snake took off? One minute it was there, and the next it was gone."

Laughter erupts as they recall the memory.

"I remember that." Gilgal looks around the table. "I got an earful from Mother later that night about not scaring the help—but I couldn't resist. It was such a sight."

"And one I have not forgotten," Suyana returns, grinning at her husband.

"I remember Mother having us pick up the clothes from the ground and put it in the basket to carry back to Fatima."

"It was a heavy basket." Enon wipes the tears from his eyes. "But so worth it."

Father sighs and looks at Emara. "It is time, Emara. Gather what you want to take while the boys ready the horses in the stable. Mother, help the women."

Suyana nods. The men get up from the table and head out

the door, leaving the women sitting. A silent tear falls down Suyana's cheek. She looks at Emara and brushes it quickly away. Loyola gets up from the table and heads to her room to gather her gear while Emara and Suyana walk to Emara's room arm in arm.

"Mother, what am I going to do without you?"

"What am I going to do without you? I am going to miss you so much." They cry in each other's arms.

Suyana sniffs and takes a steadying breath, gently touching Emara's face with her hand. "You are a woman now, which means it is time to stand. We need to hurry."

Emara nods.

Emara must be outside the gates of Uthal at sunrise or she forfeits her life. Emara grabs another dress to add to her pack while Mother hands her some things. "You must take this."

Emara looks to find the shirt and shoes her mother had her make last year in preparation for a husband. Emara nods and carefully packs them, then looks around her room one last time. Taking a deep breath, Emara picks up the pack, and both mother and daughter move out the bedroom door.

They stop by Loyola's room, where Loyola stands ready with her pack. Mother gives Loyola a hug, then turns, leading the way to the courtyard. The horses are saddled and loaded with supplies. Hezekiah and Telah get the packs from Emara and Loyola and load them on the mare, and Helam and Selina show up for the occasion.

Loyola says goodbye first, presenting the queen and the king with a gift.

"This is really good. Thank you so much for providing us a picture of Emara and Enon. It will be treasured." Gilgal and Suyana give Loyola a hug, and Enon steps forward, following Loyola with his goodbyes. After Enon finishes, it's time for Emara to say farewell.

She takes a deep breath to steady herself, then gives her mother and father a final hug. "I love you both." She hugs each brother who is staying in Uthal and ends at Selina.

"I shall miss you, Emmy." Selina throws her arms around her while trying to contain her tears.

"I will miss you too." Emara sniffs. "I will send word."

Selina nods her head.

Gilgal takes a breath and frowns. "It is time, Emara. You need to go." With a heavy heart Emara climbs her mount and looks back at her family for the last time. Tears streaming down her face, she takes a steadying breath and makes the horse take off toward Uthal's gate to beat the sunrise with Loyola and Enon following her.

BEGINNING

EMARA DOES NOT LOOK BACK this time but presses forward as the tears continue to fall. She does not stop as she passes the gate but continues on toward her precipice for one last look. Riding hard, it doesn't take long to reach the base of the cliff. She wipes her tearstained face and starts climbing, hoping to have some privacy for a little while before Enon and Loyola show up. She reaches the precipice and lets out her pent-up emotions. She feels like she has now lost another thing—her family. She is on her own. She keeps telling herself that she has Enon and Loyola, but they too will be leaving. "How will I survive? How can I survive another loss?" She looks out over the precipice as the darkness starts to retreat. She takes some deep breaths, holding her braid, and watches the sunrise unfold before her with many colors. It's glorious. The warmth of the sun kisses her body, rejuvenating both body and spirit. She wipes away her remaining tears. "It is always darkest before the dawn. I must have hope. I must move forward . . . one step at a time." Before long two people show up, sitting quietly on each side of her. No one says a word but continues to watch as the day reveals itself. There are no plans. There is no urgency. There is just now. Emara closes her eyes, basking in the warmth of the sun.

When Emara opens her eyes, only Loyola is sitting next to her looking out over the precipice. "It's beautiful up here. I'm glad Enon knew where to find you. The way you took off, I didn't think we would be able to catch up." Emara just looks at Loyola. "I know where you are at, Emara. There has been another change in your life. One that has left a deep void."

After a pregnant pause, Emara looks at Loyola. "Yes, but thanks to you, there is always hope. I must keep moving forward one step at a time."

"You understand!"

"It was hard to say goodbye."

"It's always hard to say goodbye, but that also makes a reunion that much sweeter."

"Why are you so wise?"

"Experience." Loyola grins at Emara. "Are you ready to start?"

"Yes, before my stomach starts making noises." Emara grins, brushing away one remaining tear as it escapes from her eye.

Loyola grins back. "Good. I have Enon making breakfast at the bottom of this cliff. Shall we go?" Loyola joins Emara on the descent.

When they reach the bottom of the cliff, Enon is roasting a snake over a fire. "I don't know about you, but I'm hungry." He dishes out some snake into bowls and passes it around. While the snake is cooling, Enon pulls out a prickly pear and cuts it into thirds to give each of them a piece. They eat in silence.

After their breakfast, Enon looks to Emara. "Where to, Emmy?"

"I'd like to get some herbs on the way to bring back to Arnac. It shouldn't take very long, and then we can determine where to camp when we are tired of riding." They pack up their gear and set out with Emara leading the way. They spend the morning gathering the herbs and seeds that Emara wants to take to Arnac. "If I can get the herbs to grow at Arnac, then it will be an easier source than finding it in the forest." Loyola and Enon follow her in good spirits.

Midafternoon, the lull of the horses' pace is not doing anything to keep them awake. Loyola looks to the others. "Would you mind if we stop for the day? I can barely keep my eyes open."

Enon and Emara both agree with Loyola and search for a place to make camp. One soon comes into view, and the group stops. Enon puts up the tents while Emara takes care of the horses and Loyola works on dinner. They eat dinner in silence, after which they clean their bowls and spoons and pack them back up for tomorrow. One by one they climb into their tent to sleep as exhaustion overtakes them.

Enon is the first one up the next morning and starts the day tending to the hungry horses. Loyola is second to wake up, coming out of the tent to start a fire. There is no need to hurry back to Arnac, so Loyola and Enon sit around the fire talking quietly among themselves while Loyola prepares breakfast of some dried fruit and nuts mixed with mush. Emara finally awakens and eats what is left over. After the meal, they pack up their gear and continue their trek toward Arnac.

Each day is peaceful for the three travelers as they work together traveling back to Arnac. When they get up in the mountains close to Arnac, Emara starts stopping along the path to pick something or unearth something to be used later in the day in their meals, which provides variety to their dwindling supplies and makes both Loyola and Enon grateful for her expertise. Tomorrow they will arrive at Arnac, and seeing this is their last night together, they linger longer, talking about their plans.

"Tomorrow we will arrive at Arnac," Enon says.

"That's good. Now you can be joined."

"After you're happy at Arnac."

"I know you've been talking a lot among yourselves. Have you decided where you're going to live?"

"Loyola and I have decided to live in Xenu. With Ammon missing, her father will be in need of some assistance."

"That makes sense. Are you worried that they may not accept you?" Emara's hand reaches for her braid and starts fiddling with the end of it.

"I'm not concerned. It's Loyola who has to put up with me." Enon grabs one of Loyola's hands. "We shall be fine."

"What will you do in Xenu?"

"I will serve the king of Xenu. As long as Loyola and I get to be together and work as a team, everything else will work out."

"You both work well together."

"It's late. I'll see you in the morning." Loyola gets up, moving toward the tent.

When Loyola is out of earshot, Enon turns to Emara. "What is bothering you, Emara?"

"How do you know something is bothering me?"

"Your hands are fiddling with your braid."

Emara looks down, surprised her fingers are wrapped around her braid, then looks back at her brother with a frown. "Oh." She looks down, removing her fingers from her braid.

"You're always so sure of yourself. You have so much faith." Emara throws a stick in the fire. "I always worry about everything. Tomorrow you'll be free to join Loyola, which is wonderful, and I'll stay at Arnac creating a new life for myself."

"What about Ammon?" Enon asks.

"It's close to a moon since he disappeared. Perhaps my time with him was limited to just that."

"Is that what's bothering you?" Emara nods. "Keep hope alive, Emmy. We still don't know if he's returned to Arnac, and we'll find that out tomorrow." He pats her on the shoulder. "Loyola is right that it's late. Get some sleep, and things will look better in the morning." Emara nods, getting to her feet, and her brother follows, giving her a comforting hug.

"Good night, Enon." Enon stays by the fire until it burns low, considering how he can help Emara. He finally shrugs, douses the fire, and goes into his tent to sleep.

The next morning, Emara feels more positive about the day. Enon, Loyola, and she, make quick work in getting back on the road with anticipation of reaching Arnac in a few hours. "I'm glad we are almost done traveling. I look forward to the warm spring and clean clothes."

"The warm spring is amazing. I am going to miss that when we leave Arnac."

"What warm spring? What is it?" Enon looks at the women as they daydream.

Loyola turns her face toward Enon. "Inside the city of women, hot water comes out of the ground and is channeled to various spots within the city for the women to have warm baths."

"Why don't the men have that?"

Loyola grins. "Then they would never leave."

The forest is beautiful. Every time Emara is on this road, she is amazed by what lives here. She recalls when Ammon was with her the first time on the trail and how awestruck she was with its beauty. "I still am." Turning the last bend, they see the walls of Arnac, and the weary party moves forward to go through the tunnel. A woman hollers from above, and Loyola returns the salute. Then the gates open before them.

Entering Arnac, they find the courtyard full of men and tents with different banners. Emara and Loyola are concerned and move forward quickly to hear what is going on. Seeing Calene, the party dismounts, moving toward her. She has a smile on her face.

Loyola reaches her first. "What is going on?"

Calene laughs. "We are getting ready for your Joining. Both families arrived yesterday. Now everyone is here." She gives each member of the party a hug. "Follow me." She turns, leading the way to the hall, where an assortment of guards mull around. Their colors look familiar to the three of them for different reasons. Calene continues forward with purpose, finally stopping and stepping aside to reveal Loyola's family and Enon and Emara's family, which includes Helam and Selina. A wonderful reunion takes place as Calene stands back and watches.

Enon gives his father a big hug. "Why are you here? How?"

"We did not want to miss your Joining." King Gilgal smiles at him. "After you left with Emara, Mother and I could not rest. We thought we would catch up with you on the road, but now it looks like we passed you up. How did that occur?"

"Emara wanted to gather some herbs before we started back to Arnac." Father nods and smiles. "Who is watching the city?"

"Lahonti."

"Selina's father will do a good job."

Surprised to find her parents, Loyola gives them a warm hug and talks to them while Enon and Emara talk with their family. "Why are you in Arnac?"

"When you sent someone to pick up the shirt and shoes for the Joining, we knew we had to come." Loyola's mother, Queen Quila, gives her daughter another hug.

Emara realizes that Ammon is missing and walks to Calene with the question in her eyes. Calene shakes her head. Emara takes a deep breath to steady herself. "Today is Enon and Loyola's day." Calene gently squeezes Emara's forearm.

Loyola introduces Enon and Emara to her parents. The king of Xenu, King Pachacuti, takes Emara's hand. "My son will return."

Emara nods, blinking back her tears. "Today is Loyola and Enon's day." She smiles at King Pachacuti.

"Enon, it is so good to meet you. I am glad my daughter has accepted your necklace. Where will you live after you are joined?"

"We have decided to live in Xenu."

"This makes us very happy. We have missed her."

After everyone has had time to be introduced and re-introduced, Calene claps her hands, interrupting the reunion. "It is time to prepare. Women, follow me." Calene takes Loyola's hand and leads the way. The queens and their daughters follow Calene. She stops after a few paces, looking back at Enon. "Prepare yourself, Enon. We will be back in a little while."

"For what?"

"For your Joining." Calene smiles, watching the reaction on Enon's face. She laughs and continues out the door

"I am Joining Loyola." The men usher Enon back to the courtyard to help him prepare for the Joining.

The women are taken to the quarters where Emara and

Suyana stayed. Their packs are already there and unpacked. Mothers and daughters work together to find the items Loyola needs to prepare herself while Emara and Loyola are ushered into the bathing room. While they are bathing, clothes are pulled out and arranged for each girl. Queen Quila, Loyola's mother, has her two younger daughters dress, then turns to Queen Suyana. "Would you be willing to do their hair while I change?"

Suyana nods, after which Quila changes into her best dress.

While all this is going on, Emara and Loyola enjoy the warmth of the spring, which soothes their sore muscles. When they get out of their bath, they pass between them the oil containing herbs that makes their skin and hair smell fragrant.

"Not much time to rest since we arrived," Loyola says.

"None at all. Are you happy Calene arranged it this way?"

"I'm happy to see my family and have them here, and I'm happy to be joined to Enon. I only wish Ammon could be here to be a part of it."

"He would be here if he could." They hold hands for a moment before two dressed mothers come in, interrupting. Gathering their daughters, the queens fuss over them, helping them to get into their dresses for the ceremony.

Loyola looks at the beautiful dress she now wears. "Mother, this is a beautiful dress. Where did you get it?"

"Calene provided it for you to wear."

Both young women, now dressed, sit in a chair while each mother fixes her daughter's hair. Loyola's sisters watch her from a distance, smiling, and Loyola makes a funny face just for them, making them giggle. Once Emara and Loyola's hair is styled, both daughters turn the table, making sure their mothers' hair is equally presentable. Emara gives one of Loyola's sisters the shirt and the other the shoes. Both mothers stand on each side of Loyola while Emara brings up the rear with the two younger sisters in front of her. They walk back to the hall. At the door that opens to the hall, they find Calene dressed in a brightly colored dress just as elaborate as the dresses she gave Loyola and Emara. Calene stands in the doorway, notifying everyone in the hall that it is time for the ceremony to begin. Both men and women fill the room, awaiting the Joining ceremony. Fathers and sons stand in the middle of the room awaiting the women, and it looks like King Gilgal is officiating. Calene starts toward the middle of the room with the women following. The mothers each have one of Loyola's arms while they advance into the room. Loyola's sisters follow, holding the clothing, and Emara brings up the rear. When Loyola reaches the middle of the room, Enon kneels at her feet and bows while Loyola lovingly smiles at him.

There's a commotion from the door to the courtyard as people start whispering, and all eyes go to the filthy man with ragged clothing walking purposefully toward the center of the room. He uses a pole to steady himself and has a worn, broken-down pack on his back. His face is hairy and looks like he has not eaten in days. He continues forward with purpose until he falls to his knees in front of Emara. She goes to help him up when in a loud voice he speaks. "I am Ammon, son of King Pachacuti, king of Xenu, and I desire Emara for my wife. I love her and cannot live without her in my life. Please accept my humble offering."

Emara, surprised, looks briefly at her family, then back to the man kneeling before her. She kneels down next to this man and cups his face, looking into his tired blue eyes—Ammon's eyes. She lovingly smiles at him, and he smiles back, falling unconscious into Emara's arms. Emara holds him in her arms as orders are given to take him to the infirmary. Both queens take a look at him, determining that there is no injury and seeing nothing serious is wrong with him that food, water, and rest won't fix. They stand aside so that Ammon can be moved.

The commotion of Ammon's return during the Joining brings the ceremony to a standstill as Ammon's care becomes priority. Fathers watch as Emara's brothers pick up Ammon and the queens lead the way to the infirmary. The rest of the family follows behind, wanting to help where they can. There will be no ceremony today.

HEALING

EMARA STAYS IN THE INFIRMARY watching over Ammon with both mothers. They ask her to go repeatedly, explaining she can't help any more than they can, but she retorts that she can't leave him.

"At least change your clothes," Suyana says, "and then you can return."

She finally concedes to Mother's wishes, quickly completing the task. When the mothers see her again, they nod their heads and finally let her see Ammon. Ammon has been cleaned, his face has been shaved, and he now lies on a bed with a sheet covering him. His legs are elevated. Emara looks to her mother for an update.

"He is unconscious, just like you were when you returned to Arnac. He needs fluids first, then everything else will come with time."

Emara sits on the chair next to his bed and takes over his care. "You have made it back to Arnac, and you have made it this far. Please come back to me, Ammon. It has been hard without you." She forces fluids in intervals like her mother taught her, waiting for her man to wake up.

In the middle of the night Emara is dozing in her chair beside the bed when something touches her hand, stirring her awake. She opens her eyes to find a hand clasped around hers, and she looks at Ammon's face. He still looks gaunt, but his tired blue eyes are open in the dark, moving Emara to get him some broth to drink.

After drinking, Ammon takes a breath and swallows. "How long have I been out?"

"It has been many hours. Are you hungry?"

He shakes his head. "Are we joined?"

"No, you passed out shortly after your announcement, and my brothers carried you to the infirmary."

"Oh." He looks at her. "Did I ruin your ceremony?"

"I don't understand." Emara helps him with a cup of water.

Ammon takes a drink. "Did you choose another"—he swallows—"husband?"

"Did you see the necklace I wear . . . and am still wearing?"

"No, I only saw your face. I had to make it back to you."

"The necklace I still wear is the one you gave me. See?" Emara touches the necklace around her throat. "It was Loyola who was Joining with my brother, Enon. The Joining has been postponed until you are better. I think she is all right with that, but I'm not so sure about Enon." She grins at him. "What made you think it was me getting Joined?"

"When I arrived at the gate, I was told you were in Arnac. Another person told me that a Joining was taking place. I saw my father's banner and thought he must be looking for me. I saw Uthal colors and thought your parents would only be here for a Joining, so it had to be for you. I then saw you in the hall . . ." Ammon swallows and takes a few breaths. "It's good to see you."

"You as well. I've missed you so much." Tears well up in her eyes.

"Don't cry, Emmy." His grip on her hand becomes firmer. "I don't ever want us to be separated again."

"I don't either." A tear falls down her cheek.

Ammon closes his eyes and rests for a minute. "Did you take the Challenge?"

"Yes."

"Why?"

"Because you weren't with me."

"Before my . . . disappearance, you were still going to take the Challenge . . . stating you were not ready for a husband." Ammon opens his eyes, looking directly at her. "Are you still not ready for a husband?"

"I said that because I had questions. I was not ready, but now . . ." When she looks at Ammon, his eyes are closed and his breathing is rhythmic. Emara sighs. "At least he woke up for a little bit." She wipes another stray tear from her cheek.

The morning comes, bringing both families to the infirmary. "Ammon woke up during the night and drank some broth and water before becoming unconscious again."

Queen Quila takes her hand. "Did he say anything?"

Emara looks at Ammon's mother. "Nothing of importance. It was mainly questions that I answered."

Loyola comes next to her mother and looks at Emara. "Would you like to go and get some rest while we watch over Ammon?"

Emara shakes her head, then offers a half smile, thanking them for their offer. "I need to be here with him."

Suyana comes forward. "You did well, dear. Let us know when he awakens again." The family spends a little time around Ammon, and Emara returns to her chair, working on some embroidery while she waits. After the families leave again, the area around his bed is quiet. Before long she closes her eyes, resting them for a moment with the needlework on her lap while her hand still holds the needle.

"Ow!" EMARA'S EYES FLY OPEN and she jumps off the chair, startled but ready to protect Ammon. Her needlework falls to the floor. "What happened?"

Ammon, now wide awake, has a finger in his mouth. Quila, Suyana, and Loyola rush to the other side of the bed, hearing the commotion.

Pulling the bleeding finger out of his mouth, Ammon responds hoarsely, "I reached for your hand and got stabbed by something." The four females look at him for a minute, trying to figure out what he's talking about.

Emara's eyes light up as comprehension dawns. "Oh!" Emara reaches down and picks up the embroidery, showing it to the others before placing it to the side.

Quila sits on the side of the bed, looking at the injured finger, which has already stopped bleeding. "It is good to see you." She kisses the injured finger. "Your finger will be fine." Emara tries to hide a grin as she hands a cup of broth to Quila. "Drink, son."

Ammon looks at the women around him and then back to his mother. He drinks what is in the cup as Loyola moves to sit on the other side of the bed, smiling at her brother. When Ammon is done drinking the broth, he looks at Loyola. "Sorry to have interrupted your Joining, but I'm glad I stopped it. I want to be present for it."

"I'm so glad you're back because I want you there as well. What happened to you?"

Emara, knowing this is time for family, starts walking away from the bed to allow them some privacy.

"Don't go," Ammon says.

All eyes move to Emara.

"I wanted to give you some privacy."

"Don't go."

Quila looks at her son and looks at Emara. "Please, Emara, come and sit with us." Quila motions to the chair Emara recently vacated and watches as Emara returns and sits down.

"May I have some water?"

Emara fills the cup and helps him hold it as he drinks. When he's finished, Emara returns the cup and sits again.

Ammon's hand searches for her hand and grasps it firmly. "Loyola, I will answer when Father arrives. Mother, it's so good to see you again. I'm so glad that you've had a chance to meet Emara. This is who I choose."

"It looks as if she has chosen you too." Quila smiles at her son.

"How long do I have to be here?"

"A few days, maybe longer, depending on how much rest you get and the fluids you drink. Is there anything you want or need?"

Ammon looks lovingly at Emara. "It's all right here."

"I will leave the two of you." Quila gives her son a kiss on the forehead. "Drink, Ammon, and rest. I will bring your father later this afternoon." She leaves the area, returning to what she was doing in the infirmary.

"Ammon, I'm so glad you are back with us." Loyola gives her brother a quick hug and grins. "Follow Mother's orders if you want to get out of here." She stands up, leaving to join her mother.

"Your mother is correct," Emara says. "You really need to drink and rest. Do you think you can take some more?"

Ammon looks at Emara and nods, then Emara supplies the broth to drink. When he is done drinking again, Emara returns the cup to the table. "I don't like being like this."

"No one does." Emara sits on the side of the bed to face him.

"I fell asleep as you were answering my question. I'm sorry for that." He takes her hand again, rubbing it affectionately. "I recall you telling me you had questions. What questions, Emara?"

Emara awkwardly chuckles. "There were a lot of questions, but they are resolved now."

"You're a deep thinker, and all those questions matter. Will you please share them with me?"

"If you insist, but you must drink."

Ammon nods his head.

"Before we start with the questions, I must lay the background."

He nods his head for her to proceed.

Emara tells Ammon about her growing-up years and working in the infirmary, where she saw many different things, including bad spouses. "I want the kind of Joining my parents and your parents have. It's one of love, kindness, and respect, which I found with you after my injury. You made me feel safe and respected during my convalescence. We work well together, and you make me happy. You even learned to listen to me. Once I was better, we had to continue to work together to make it back to Arnac. My questions stemmed from the unknowns regarding the future. When life got back to normal, would you still make me happy? Would you still make me feel safe, respected, and loved? Would you still listen to me? Would I be happy away from my family? What would I do in Xenu? Would your parents accept me for who I am and not for some idea of what your wife should be?" Emara sighs and sees Ammon is about to speak. "Don't speak. Just drink." She gets the cup of water and helps him as he drinks again. When he is done, she returns to sitting on the bed. He takes her hand again, affectionately holding it.

"I want us to continue to be friends, like our parents. I like answers, and I had none at the time. Our walk back to Arnac helped me settle some things." Emara grins. "Guard duty is great for working through issues." She looks down for a moment, gathering her thoughts, then looks up, frowning. "When I lost you over the ledge, I lost a portion of myself—I lost the man I love. I went to a dark place, and I lost hope. Some of my concerns that I had didn't matter anymore. My mother, Enon, and Loyola helped me through that dark time. As I healed, your sister helped answer some of those initial questions, and some answers I found with Enon."

Her eyes sparkle as she continues. "You're the crown prince of Xenu, and I am a princess who has been trained for the role of one day becoming a queen. I've met your parents, and they seem like very nice individuals." She grins again. "Especially with how well they've raised Loyola and you." She stops for a moment, formulating her words. "I will continue to get to know them better, and Loyola and Enon have decided to make their home in Xenu so family will be nearby. We work well together, and you make me happy." With love in her eyes, she smiles at Ammon. "You even listen." She pauses. "I don't know what the future brings, but this much I know: I don't want my life to be without you, Ammon. I choose you and everything that goes along with it. I choose you." Ammon brings Emara's hand to his mouth and gently kisses it. His eyes close. "It's time for you to rest." Emara stands up, but he does not release her hand.

"Not yet. We're not done. I need to tell you something because it will come out. Please sit." Emara does as he asks. "The first time I saw you was about seven years ago. I was brought to Uthal to be presented to your parents and you as your betrothed. I didn't know about the arrangement until it was announced to me when I met your parents. At first I was angry at my parents for arranging it, and I didn't want you to be forced into being my wife, so I made the deal with your parents to not tell you, making it so we were never introduced. Every year my parents made me travel to Uthal, where I was to meet with you, but instead I saw you from a distance, and I liked what I saw. I liked the smart, precocious princess who practiced and practiced to become a warrior like her brothers." Ammon looks lovingly in Emara's eyes. "I love the woman you've become."

Ammon holds her hand, patiently watching her as she absorbs the information. Finally, Emara looks up at Ammon. "When you told me that our Joining was arranged, I could not believe it, but it kept bothering me, especially since you followed me from Uthal. What were you thinking?"

"I was trying to figure out a way to meet you." He grins at her.

"I asked my mother about it and she confirmed what I already knew—that you were telling the truth. Not so long ago in Uthal, there was a woman who had not found a husband, which meant my father was involved in choosing the most appropriate person for her. I tried to give her hope, stating my father took this very seriously. When the shy man was brought forward, she knew him and was overjoyed with my father's choice. I know our parents were involved in this"—Emara tenderly smiles at Ammon—"but I like the fact that you gave me time so I could choose for myself. Thank you for that gift. I still choose you."

"Give me a few days, and we can be joined."

"Now, it's time to rest." Emara leans over and kisses him gently on the lips as he quickly falls asleep. "Sweet dreams."

In the afternoon, King Pachacuti, king of Xenu, arrives to the infirmary to see how his son is recovering. He first greets his wife, who brings him over to the bed where

Ammon sleeps and Emara sits on the chair doing her embroidery.

"How is my son?" Pachacuti asks Emara.

"He was awake several hours ago talking with Loyola and his mother. He still needs a lot of fluids and much rest."

The king nods his head. "When will he be awake?"

"When his body has received—"

"Adequate fluids," Ammon croaks, looking at his father and grinning.

"My son." The king falls to his knees next to the bed while Emara gets the cup of water and helps Ammon drink.

"You can only hear that statement so many times." Ammon grins weakly. He takes another drink of water.

"What happened to you?"

"After we fell off the cliff?"

The king nods.

"We landed in the river, and I lost my sword. At first the pack carried me down the surface of the river, separating me from the other man. Then it was a struggle to breathe because it started to sink as I moved closer to the waterfall." He breathes for a minute, mustering his strength, then continues. "I fought with everything I had to make it to shore, and later woke up on the bank, so I guess I made it." He closes his eyes for a little, summoning his strength to continue the story. "I discovered I was on the opposite side of the river, then made a plan to make another canoe with what I had left, which didn't go so well. I tried many other things to get across the river, but each one failed. Finally, food was running out, and I made another attempt, deciding to make a paddle and lash myself to a fallen log below the waterfall. That attempt brought me to this side of the river." Ammon rests again closing his eyes. After a minute he continues. "I walked back to Arnac."

"We didn't see you on the road."

"For most of the time I was not on the road." He closes his eyes to muster up strength to speak again. "I didn't make it to the road until the day I arrived in Arnac."

King Pachacuti pats his son's shoulder. "Sleep. We can talk later."

During the night, Emara sleeps on the chair next to Ammon's bed. When his hand touches hers, she awakens. After, she props him up in bed and quietly gives him some water to drink. She sits on the side of his bed while he drinks the cup of water. When he's done, she raises the cup, asking if he wants more, but he shakes his head no. She returns the cup to the table next to the bed.

"I like waking up and seeing you next to me," Ammon says while rubbing her hand affectionately.

"You're not the first guy to use that line on me in the infirmary." Emara cocks an eyebrow at him. "But, you're the first one that I believe."

"Are you good with living at Xenu? I know it's far away from your family."

"It is, but Enon and Loyola will be nearby. You stated you've been traveling to Uthal for seven years. I never saw you until the Journey."

"I made a point not to interfere with your life. When word came to me that you were intending to choose the Challenge, that gave me hope that there wasn't another who had piqued your interest. I was trying to figure out how to meet you on the Journey when the Gadianton robbers attacked."

"Thank you for helping." They sit in silence for a little while. "Mother found a turquoise stone in my pack. Did you put it there?"

"I found it in the mudslide when I dug out your pack." Ammon chuckles at the memory. "I think it was meant for you to have. If you like, I could have it made into a piece of jewelry for you to wear."

"I don't want to worry about that right now." Emara shakes her head, dismissing his suggestion. "Mother told me that the stone is only given in love."

"Because it is such a precious, sacred stone, it is only given in love. I love"—Ammon yawns—"you."

Emara smiles. "I love you too. Let me get you some fresh broth, and then you need to rest again." Emara pulls away her hand while Ammon nods, already feeling tired. Emara returns with some fresh warm broth and feeds him. After finishing most of the bowl, Ammon falls back asleep.

A FEW DAYS LATER IN the morning, Ammon is released from the infirmary. Quila and Emara accompany Ammon to the doors of a tent.

"Thank you, Mother and Emmy, for taking me to my tent."

"You still need rest, and here is a waterskin," Emara says.

"Thanks. Do you know where Enon is?"

"No, but I don't think he is far away from Loyola. Find her, and you find him."

"Mother, I need to find Enon. Emara can accompany me."

Looking at her son and then to Emara, Quila says, "Don't let him overdo it."

"I will do my best."

Quila kisses her son's cheek. "You listen to Emara. You've given your mother enough of a scare." Quila gives Emara a hug. "Thank you for taking care of my son." Then she turns, leaving them outside his tent.

Emara says, "You stay here and rest while I find Enon and bring him here."

"Let me come with you."

"Rest, Ammon. I will be back shortly." Emara squeezes his

arm and leaves him standing at the tent door with a waterskin and a frown on his face. He goes inside the tent and realizes he is still a bit weak and sits. Before long, Enon announces himself outside the tent door.

"Come in."

Enon walks inside. "Emmy found me and told me you would like to see me."

"Where are Emmy and Loyola?"

"Outside the tent."

"Get them to leave, and then we can talk."

Enon looks at him for a minute and then goes outside the tent, returning shortly thereafter. "They're gone."

"What did you tell them?"

"That I was spending the afternoon with you."

"Good. Was Emmy upset?"

"No."

"Come and sit." Ammon waits until Enon sits down. "I don't want to spend another day waiting for Emmy and me to be joined. How about you?"

"Loyola doesn't want to be joined until you can be there."

"Well, I'm out of the infirmary." He grins. "Let's go talk with our fathers and see if we can talk them into Joining us today."

"That sounds like a wonderful idea, but only if you are up for it."

Ammon raises the waterskin, taking another drink, then they both go in search of their fathers. Ammon and Enon find the patriarchs talking to one another in the hall, where they unintentionally interrupt the conversation, when they sit down next to them.

Getting the patriarchs attention, Ammon proceeds with their plea. "Fathers, Enon and I would like to be joined today.

It has been long enough, and we do not want to wait anymore."

"Ammon, you have just been released from the infirmary. Are you sure you are well enough for this?"

"I am sure."

"Let's see what Calene says." King Pachacuti summons Calene, who hears the proposal.

"Enon, is this what you want?"

"Yes."

Calene turns to Ammon. "Are you sure you are strong enough?"

"I'm stronger now. I can do this. I will heal quicker with my wife by my side than without her."

Calene turns to the two kings. "Are you both good with this?"

The kings nod in response.

"Very well." Calene smiles. "I will make it so."

It is announced that the Joining will happen this afternoon, and excitement spreads throughout Arnac.

LOYOLA AND EMARA ARE SITTING under their tree next to the pool of water talking and haven't heard the announcement when Calene finds them. "Loyola and Emara, I am glad that I have found the both of you. Hurry and come with me."

Loyola and Emara look at each other and get up, quickly following Calene. When they arrive at their quarters, Calene walks right in, revealing mothers and sisters. Calene turns to Emara and Loyola. "How do you feel about being joined right now?"

Emara confused with how to answer the question asks, "Ammon was just released from the infirmary, and Enon is staying with him today. Is he well enough?"

"It turns out that Ammon is well enough, and both would like to be joined today, if that is agreeable to you?"

Loyola and Emara look at each other, then turn to Calene with joyful grins on their faces. "Yes!" they say in unison.

"Wonderful! Then all of you must hurry. Get ready; people are waiting." The room turns into a buzz of activity, and Calene leaves. Loyola and Emara dress in the beautiful dresses that were gifts from Calene a few days before. Mothers and daughters fuss over each other, making sure they look their best. This time, Emara is one of the main people involved and is glad that she gets to have the Joining at the same time as Loyola. Flora and Palla, Loyola's younger sisters, now carry one set of clothing for each man and grin from ear to ear, standing proudly to the side and talking to one another.

Loyola looks at Emara. "You look beautiful. Are you excited?"

"Yes, and a little nervous. I'm so glad we get to do this Joining together. More eyes will be on you, since you look absolutely radiant."

Loyola laughs.

Calene comes to the room again wearing her vibrant dress and gathers the women to bring them to the hall for the ceremony. Calene, satisfied, smiles on the women as they line up. Loyola is first because she's the oldest, and she stands with a radiant smile on her face next to her mother. For Emara, what was once lost is now found, and she is overjoyed as she struggles to keep her emotions in check.

"Is this really happening or is this a dream?" Suyana pinches her. "Ow!" Emara warily eyes her mother, who smiles at her.

"It is real, Emara." She gives her daughter another smile and hug. The mothers and daughters file out the door, following Calene, with Loyola's sisters bringing up the rear.

At the hall, Calene presents herself at the doorway. When the people in the room are ready, Calene proceeds forward into the hall with Queen Quila holding Loyola's arm. Queen Suyana follows them, holding Emara's arm, and Flora and Palla bring up the rear. They stop where the fathers stand, full of pride for their children's choices. Emara and Loyola stand while Enon and Ammon kneel at their partners' feet, bowing humbly. This time Loyola's father officiates and has a huge smile on his face. King Pachacuti asks the questions of each man and woman. Each answers the questions given them.

King Pachacuti looks at Loyola and Emara. "Dress your husband." As Emara changes Ammon's shirt, her hands linger on his shoulders and chest, recalling the feel of them. Even with the loss of muscle mass, he feels good, causing her stomach to do a little dance, and she swallows. She looks at Ammon, meeting his eyes, seeing passion there, and looks away, blushing—knowing he read her thoughts. She gets his new shoes and goes to his feet. When she changes his shoes, she notices the scabs on his feet from his return trip to her, and tears come to her eyes knowing he endured so much. Great love for this man fills her chest. As gently as she can, she puts on the new shoes, trying not to hurt him as she blinks away her tears. When she is done with the shoes, she stands again in front of him. She meets Ammon's eyes to find love emanating from them and reaches out, taking Ammon's hands.

King Pachacuti tells the husbands to rise and join their wives. Ammon stands up, walking the short distance to stand close to Emara. He takes the bracelet on her left wrist and moves it to the right, then gently touches her face and kisses her deeply. A cheer goes up in the hall, interrupting the kiss. They look at their audience as a happy husband and blushing bride.

"My son, I am glad to see that you are happy with your

bride, but you need to control yourself for a little while longer." Laughter fills the room. When Enon is done changing the bracelet from Loyola's left wrist to right, King Pachacuti smiles, turning to the audience again. "I would like to introduce Ammon and Emara, and Enon and Loyola as newly joined." With new shirt and shoes, each man stands next to his wife, smiling happily as a roar goes up and music starts. Pachacuti walks the couples to chairs to sit in while guests visit with the couples and bring gifts.

When that is over, King Gilgal moves to stand between each couple while Ammon reaches for Emara's hand. "When I was newly joined," Gilgal says, "I thought that life was perfect. As crown prince, at the time, I thought that what I thought and spoke was always right. We had an arranged Joining, and I learned quickly that we did not always see eye to eye, which brought contention into our new home. At first, I thought it best to let my wife work through the disagreements herself because, of course, I was always right. After multiple days of my wife not speaking to me and being alone at night, I decided this was a bad approach, so I changed. Instead, I listened to her complaints with an open mind, like I would with any other member of the community, and I came to understand her complaints were valid. Because I listened, we were able to work through our issues, and our life became happier."

King Pachacuti puts his hand on King Gilgal's shoulder and takes his place. "My sons and daughters, your father has spoken truth. It is important to always listen to one another so you can work together. When I was newly joined, I had a problem I was trying to sort out by myself. I asked some wise men for their opinion about the problem, but their advice did not speak peace to my heart. After many days trying to figure out a solution, I was still in turmoil. In the beginning, my wife felt the weight on my shoulders and suggested I share the problem with her, and so after many days, I finally did. She was able to come up with a solution in a very short time that spoke peace to my heart. Since that time, I have always included her, which has made me a much happier man."

Others follow the two kings, dispensing their wisdom to the couples, until dinner is served, with many delicacies brought by both queens and prepared under Calene's eye. There is much dancing and eating in the hall that goes until late in the evening.

Calene finally draws the party to a close and gathers the newly joined couples together with their family. "It is a blessing to have your Joinings here at Arnac. There is much love between these two families that unites them beyond the bounds of a city." The couples stand at the pinnacle of the room overlooking the crowd. Emara has never seen such happiness fill a scene, and at this moment, she feels complete. "Tonight they start a new journey, facing new challenges together. Tonight, they become one." Those in the hall join Calene as she starts singing the Joining song. All the while, celebratory flowers and garlands are flung through the air.

Two are now joined,
Making life together, joined as one.
Man serving Woman,
Woman serving Man,
Making life together, joined as one.

THE END

FAMILIES

Pachacuti & Quila Gilgal & Suyana Lahonti & Abish
King & Queen of Xenu *King & Queen of Uthal*

Loyola Helam Ogath
Ammon Enon Selina
Flora Hezekiah Shum
Palla Telah
Emara

HISTORICAL
FACTS

THERE ARE TWO GEOGRAPHICAL HYPOTHESES regarding where the events in the Book of Mormon took place. The original location was North America, stated by Joseph Smith throughout his life.[34, 35, 36] The other popular geographical location is in Mesoamerica. This opinion came about later in history and has become prominent due in part to[2, 34, 36] some beautiful artwork depicting persons within the Book of Mormon using a Mesoamerican geography.[34] The Book of Mormon contains words such as *swords*, *horses*, *sheep*, and *linen* that are not openly accepted as historical. This book is a work of fiction that attempts to identify what it was possibly like to be a girl growing up in this society. Below is some historical information that may corroborate the use of these words within this book.

According to the Book of Mormon, over 2,000 years ago an advanced civilization with a complex society lived. The people in the Book of Mormon divided their society down into two main groups, Lamanites and Nephites,[3] which separated themselves geographically. Nephites lived north of the Lamanites.[2] What remains today is an abridged 1,000 years of history, their posterity—the American Indians—and a few archeological items.

Hopewell Indians—The Hopewell Indian name originated from a man named Mordecai Hopewell, whose land contained mounds that were excavated in the 1800s.[1, 2] The Book of Mormon retrieved from the Hill Cumorah, Ontario County, New York[37] was located in the region inhabited by the Hopewell Indians.[38] The Book of Mormon contains an abridged 1,000-year historical record that was translated in the 1800s.[3] They built their cities using wood and dirt,[4, 5, 32] and, over 2,000 years, the remains of their civilization have all but disappeared. Since they were an advanced civilization, I gave them stairs and second-story buildings.

Weapons—The Hopewell culture knew how to work metal.[27] Swords are mentioned throughout the Book of Mormon as a weapon of choice during their wars between the two factions.[39] There are two types of swords mentioned in this book. One is what is known is the gunstock war club,[14] and another is something similar to what is known as a maquahuitl sword.[12, 13]

Eye Color—The perception is that Native American Indians only have black hair and brown eyes. While this is a dominant characteristic, it is not the case for every American Indian.[6, 7]

Textiles—The industry of some of the Hopewell Indians produced fine clothing.[8] Linen is mentioned multiple times in the Book of Mormon and thus is included within the contents of this book.[11]

Society—I found a complex society based upon different

tribes utilizing the Book of Mormon and other historical sources.[9, 10] I decided to use some of these differences within the different cities mentioned in the book.

Sheep and Horses—The Book of Mormon mentions horses a multitude of times.[15] Bones of horses[16, 28, 29, 30] and sheep[17] have been discovered in North America and Canada after the last ice age and before Columbus.

Food and Herbs—The Book of Mormon contains reference to food.[18] I think they also planted and harvested many other things, using the resources around them to create variety to their diet and improve health just like we do today. I have provided some indigenous foods and herbs that are native to North America in an effort to enhance the story.[19, 20, 21, 22, 23, 24, 25, 26]

The Joining—There is no reference to marriages or the ceremony within the Book of Mormon nor in any historical document that has been found. Taking the context of some tribes' ideology and ceremonies for marriage, I have tried to move that back two thousand years to create what possibly could have occurred with regard to arranged marriage, non-arranged marriage, and ceremony in the Lamanite culture within the Hopewell Indians.

REFERENCES

1. The Archaeological Institute of America. (2009). *Who were the Hopewell*. Archeology. https://archive. archaeology.org/online/features/hopewell/ who_were_hopewell.html
2. Neville, J. (2016). *Moroni's America*. Digital Legend.
3. Mormon. (1989). *The Book of Mormon* (J. Smith, trans.). The Church of Jesus Christ of Latter-day Saints. https://www.churchofjesuschrist.org/study/scriptures/ bofm/bofm-title?lang=eng
    Title page
4. Mormon. (1989). *The Book of Mormon* (J. Smith, trans.). The Church of Jesus Christ of Latter-day Saints. Retrieved from https://www.churchofjesuschrist.org/study/ scriptures/bofm/bofm-title?lang=eng
    City walls: Alma 53:4, Alma 49:2
5. Squier, E. G., & Davis, E. H. (2015 August 10). *The Project Gutenberg EBook of Ancient Monuments of the*

Mississippi Valley. Retrieved from http://www.gutenberg.
org/files/49668/49668-h/49668-h.htm

6. DNA Consultants. (2018). U.S. Cherokee. Retrieved
    from https://dnaconsultants.com/cherokee-1/

7. Swancer, B. (2017 October 13). *The mysterious tribe
    of blue-eyed Native Americans*. Mysterious Universe.
    https://mysteriousuniverse.org/2017/10/
    the-mysterious-tribe-of-blue-eyed-native-americans/

8. Kakima. (n.d.). *The Hopewell Culture of Ohio: Teach-
    ing Native American History*. Bright Hub Education.
    https://www.brighthubeducation.com/
    middle-school-social-studies-lessons/
    67881-teaching-students-about-the-hopewell-native-
    american-culture/

9. TeachingHistory.org. (2018). *American Indian women*.
    Teaching History. https://teachinghistory.org/
    history-content/ask-a-historian/23931

10. Encyclopaedia Britannica. (2019). The Hopewell
    culture: North American Indian culture. In *Encyclo-
    paedia Britannica*. https://www.britannica.com/topic/
    Hopewell-culture

11. Mormon. (1989). *The Book of Mormon* (J. Smith, trans.).
    The Church of Jesus Christ of Latter-day Saints.
    https://www.churchofjesuschrist.org/study/scriptures/
    bofm/bofm-title?lang=eng
    Cloth: Helaman 6:13, Alma 1:29, Alma 4:6; Mosiah 10:5

12. Native Languages of the Americas. (2015). *Native
    American Indian weapons*. Native-Languages.org. http://
    www.native-languages.org/weapons.htm

13. Squier, E. G., & Davis, E. H. (2015 August 10). *The
    Project Gutenberg EBook of Ancient Monuments of the
    Mississippi Valley*. Retrieved from http://www.gutenberg.
    org/files/49668/49668-h/49668-h.htm

14. Jeffccoat, T. L. (2013). Weapons and warriors: Gunstock warclub of the Native Americans. *Sailing on the Astral Sea*. http://mrtalkstoomuch.blogspot.com/2013/12/weapons-warriors-gunstock-war-club-of.html

15. Mormon. (1989). *The Book of Mormon* (J. Smith, trans.). The Church of Jesus Christ of Latter-day Saints. https://www.churchofjesuschrist.org/study/scriptures/bofm/bofm-title?lang=eng
Horses: Alma 18:9-10, 12, 1 Nephi 18:25, Alma 20:6, 3 Nephi 6:1, 3 Nephi 4:4, 3 Nephi 3:22

16. Jones, S. E. (2012). Were there horses in the Americas before Columbus? *The Wild Horse Conspiracy*. https://thewildhorseconspiracy.org/2013/07/02/exciting-article-about-by-phd-steven-jones-re-more-recent-surviving-native-horse-in-north-america/

17. National Bighorn Sheep Center. (2018). *About bighorns*. Bighorn.org. https://bighorn.org/about-bighorns/

18. Mormon. (1989). *The Book of Mormon* (J. Smith, trans.). The Church of Jesus Christ of Latter-day Saints. https://www.churchofjesuschrist.org/study/scriptures/bofm/bofm-title?lang=eng Food: Mosiah 9:9

19. Shreeves, R. (2018). *America's only native pepper may be small, but it's fiery hot*. Mother Nature Network. https://www.mnn.com/food/healthy-eating/blogs/chiltepin-americas-only-native-pepper-small-fiery-hot

20. Kiprop, V. (2019 July 5). Fruits native to North America. *WorldAtlas*. https://www.worldatlas.com/articles/fruits-native-to-north-america.html

21. Foodtank. (2016). 20 native North American foods with stories to tell. *FoodTank*. https://foodtank.com/news/2016/07/indigenous-foods-historically-and-culturally-important-to-north-americ/

22. Havard, V. (1895). Food plants of the North American Indians. *Bulletin of the Torrey Botanical Club, 22*(3), 98–123. doi:10.2307/2477757. https://www.jstor.org/stable/2477757?seq=1#metadata_info_tab_contents

23. MacWelch, T. (2014 May 27). *Survival skills: 14 wild medicinal plants*. Outdoor Life. https://www.outdoorlife.com/blogs/survivalist/2014/05/survival-skills-14-wild-medicinal-plants/

24. Kellner, J. (2016 November/December). *Native American plants and medicinal herbs: Discover the benefits of five of North America's most-researched healing native plants.* Mother Earth Living. https://www.motherearthliving.com/health-and-wellness/natural-remedies/native-american-plants-zm0z16ndzfol

25. Polizzi, N. (2018 March 24). 3 Powerful indigenous herbs from North America. *The Sacred Science.* https://www.thesacredscience.com/3-powerful-indigenous-herbs-from-north-america/

26. Stritch, L. (n.d.). Plant of the week: Wild ginger (*Asarum canadense L.*). U.S. Forest Service. https://www.fs.fed.us/wildflowers/plant-of-the-week/asarum_canadense.shtml

27. Mormon. (1989). *The Book of Mormon* (J. Smith, trans.). The Church of Jesus Christ of Latter-day Saints. https://www.churchofjesuschrist.org/study/scriptures/bofm/bofm-title?lang=eng
Metal work: 1 Nephi 17:11; Helaman 6:11

28. Johnson, D. (2015). "Hard" evidence of ancient American horses. *BYU Studies, 54*(3), 149–179. https://byustudies.byu.edu/content/hard-evidence-ancient-american-horses

29. Johnston, L. J. (2019). Yes world, there were horses in Native culture before the settlers came. *Indian Country*

Today. https://newsmaven.io/indiancountrytoday/news/
yes-world-there-were-horses-in-native-culture-before-
the-settlers-came-JGqPrqLmZk-3ka-IBqNWiQ/

30. The Horse Fund (2013). Indian horses before Columbus. *Tuesday's Horse.* https://tuesdayshorse.wordpress.
com/2013/10/14/indian-horses-before-columbus/

31. 8 Humanities. (n.d.). *Woodland Indians: Iroquois and
Algonquin.* 8 Humanities. http://8bishumanities.weebly.
com/woodland-indians-iroquois-and-algonquin1.html

32. Weiser, K. (2020). *Cahokia Mounds, Illinois—Largest
archaeological site in North America.* Legends of America.
https://www.legendsofamerica.com/il-cahokia/

33. Platt, D. (2012). *Hopewell Culture National Historical Park: Seip Mound* Trek Ohio. https://trekohio.
com/2012/07/27/seip-mound-at-hopewell-culture-
national-historical-park/

34. Book of Mormon Evidence. (2019 October 11).
The smoking gun of Book of Mormon geography.
Bookofmormonevidence.org https://bookofmormon-
evidence.org/the-smoking-gun-of-book-of-mormon-
geography-2/

35. J. Smith to E. Smith. (4 June 1834). Retrieved from
https://www.josephsmithpapers.org/paper-summary/
letter-to-emma-smith-4-june-1834/3

36. Book of Mormon Evidence, (2019 October 14). Joseph
Smith knew Book of Mormon geography. Bookofmor-
monevidence.org https://bookofmormonevidence.org/
joseph-smith-knew-book-of-mormon-geography/

37. Mormon. (1989). The Book of Mormon (J. Smith,
trans.). The Church of Jesus Christ of Latter-day Saints.
https://www.churchofjesuschrist.org/study/scriptures/
bofm/js?lang=eng Testimony of the Prophet Joseph
Smith

REFERENCES

38. Legends of America (2020). Hopewell Culture of Native Americans. https://www.legendsofamerica.com/hopewell-culture/
39. Mormon. (1989). The Book of Mormon (J. Smith, trans.). The Church of Jesus Christ of Latter-day Saints. https://www.churchofjesuschrist.org/study/scriptures/bofm/bofm-title?lang=eng
Swords: Alma 17:7, Alma 44:8, Alma 60:2 to name a few.
40. Center for Digital Research in the Humanities. (n.d.). Ohio Hopewell: Ancient crossroads of the American Midwest. http://hopewell.unl.edu/images.html

ABOUT THE AUTHOR

As a child, Monica Flores hated reading and all things that fall under the subject of English. She didn't become a book worm until she was a teenager, when introduced to Jane Austen's *Pride and Prejudice*. Since that time, Monica has become an avid reader. During the day, she works as a nurse at the county hospital. She enjoys serving in her church and community, spending time with friends and family, doing family history work, eating chocolate and, of course, reading books.

Made in the USA
Coppell, TX
04 August 2020

32453380R00173